Y 546.421 ACT

4/08
7/09
8/11
3/11
11/14

Actinium to Fluorine

Please check all items for damages
before leaving the Library.
Thereafter you will be held
responsible for all injuries
to items beyond reasonable wear.

Helen M. Plum Memorial Library

Lombard, Illinois

A daily fine will be charged for
overdue materials.

NOV   2005

Elements

Actinium
to Fluorine

Grolier Educational

How to use this set

The *Elements* set has been carefully developed to help you understand the chemistry of the elements. Volumes 1 to 15 provide an in-depth look at the 32 best-known elements.

Volumes 16 to 18 outline the properties, uses, discovery, technology, geology, and biology of all the elements known up to 118. There is also a key facts table of comparative data for each element.

Volumes 16 to 18 present the elements in alphabetical order, with the full name of the element and its symbol (e.g., americium—Am). Frequently, an element's symbol derives from a different word than its common name. For instance, Ag (from the Latin word *argentum*) is the symbol for silver. To help you find these elements by symbol, the symbols appear alphabetically at the tops of appropriate pages. For example, Ag appears on the page for aluminum and points you to silver: Ag *see* Silver.

At the back of each volume is a glossary and an index to all 18 volumes in the set.

Aluminum is an excellent conductor of electricity and is used extensively in cables.

. . . .

Author
Brian Knapp, BSc, PhD
Project consultant
Keith B. Walshaw, MA, BSc, DPhil
Art Director
Duncan McCrae, BSc
Editors
Mary Sanders, BSc, and Gillian Gatehouse
Special photography
Ian Gledhill
Illustrations
David Woodroffe
Designed and produced by
EARTHSCAPE EDITIONS
Reproduced in Malaysia by
Global Colour Separation
Printed in Hong Kong by
Wing King Tong Company Ltd

First published in the United States in 2002 by Grolier Educational, Sherman Turnpike, Danbury, CT 06816

Y
546.421
A CT

Cataloging information may be obtained directly from Grolier Educational.

Volumes 1-18 Set ISBN: 0–7172–5674–X
Volumes 16-18 Set ISBN: 0–7172–5675–8
Volume 16 ISBN: 0–7172–5676–6
Library of Congress Number: 95–082222
Dewey: 546—dc21

Acknowledgments
The publishers would like to thank the following for their kind help and advice: *Kjc Operating Company* and *Michael Barrett.*

Picture credits
All photographs are from the **Earthscape Editions** photolibrary except the following:
(c=center t=top b=bottom l=left r=right)
UKAEA Technology 32b.

Title page: Chromium is resistant to corrosion in air, and chrome plating is used to coat and protect metals such as iron and steel.

This product is manufactured from sustainable managed forests. For every tree cut down at least one more is planted.

The demonstrations described or illustrated in this book are not for replication. The Publisher cannot accept any responsibility for any accidents or injuries that may result from conducting the experiments described or illustrated in this book.

Contents

Introduction

An element is a substance that cannot be broken down into simpler substances by any known means. There are at least 118 elements, of which 92 occur in stable, natural forms on Earth, and 26 can be made in the laboratory and may possibly occur naturally elsewhere in the universe. These elements are the fundamental materials from which everything in the universe is made. Most elements are metals, but 16 are described as nonmetals and 9 as metalloids.

Atoms

Elements are composed of atoms. A piece of sulfur is made entirely of sulfur atoms, and a lump of iron is made entirely of iron atoms. When in a pure state, an element is described as elemental.

Elements can be combined in a chemical reaction to form compounds, or they can be blended to form mixtures. There are millions of possible compounds that can be made.

Each element is represented by a symbol, such as S for sulfur, Fe for iron, or Ca for calcium, and so on.

Atoms are made up of three kinds of particles. In the center, or nucleus, there are two kinds, protons and neutrons. Surrounding the nucleus are electrons (often visualized as orbiting, much like planets around the Sun).

Abundance of the elements	
Element	% of Universe
Hydrogen	87
Helium	12
Oxygen	0.06
Carbon	0.03
Neon	0.02
Nitrogen	0.008
Silicon	0.003
Iron	0.002
Sulfur	0.002
Argon	0.0004
Magnesium	0.0003
Aluminum	0.0002
Calcium	0.0001
Sodium	0.0001
Phosphorus	0.00003
Potassium	0.000007

The number of protons in each element is unique. The number of protons in an element is called its atomic number. An atom of iron, for example, has 26 protons in its nucleus, and so its atomic number is 26. The number of protons, in turn, is equal to the number of electrons surrounding the nucleus. Iron has 26 electrons.

Once the atomic number is known, all of the elements can be organized in order of increasing atomic number to make the Periodic Table (*see* pages 6-7).

The electrons that are present in an atom are racing around the nucleus. Each electron can be thought of as moving in a path that is a fixed distance from the nucleus. The chemical properties of an element depend on the number of electrons in the outermost region—called a shell—of the atom.

Scientists can draw the pattern of the electrons in what is called a shell diagram. The diagrams can be shown as a series of rings.

Scientists know that the innermost shell is very stable when it holds 2 electrons, the second shell is stable when it contains 8, the third shell is stable as an outer shell when it has 8, and so on. The shell diagrams for all of the elements are shown on the pages of this set of books.

The number of protons is always equal to the number of electrons in an atom.

Shell Diagrams

▼ An argon atom (Ar) has an atomic number of 18 and therefore has 18 protons and 18 electrons. The electrons can be arranged as shown in this shell diagram.

The nucleus at the center of the atom contains protons and neutrons. The number of protons is given by the atomic number, more recently called the proton number.

A circle with electrons represents a shell.

These show the number of electrons in each shell.

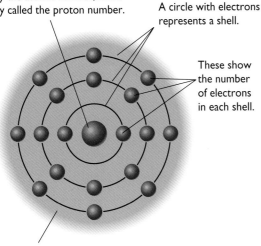

The outer shell of an argon atom is full, and so this atom does not react – it is inert.

▼ A chlorine atom (Cl) has an atomic number of 17 and therefore has 17 protons and 17 electrons. The electrons can be arranged as shown in this shell diagram.

The outer shell of a chlorine atom has seven instead of eight electrons, and so this atom is highly reactive, being strongly attractive to an electron.

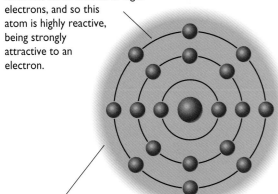

The background color shows whether the element is a metal, nonmetal, metalloid, or inner transition metal. The Periodic Table on pages 6–7 also has a color key.

The Periodic Law

The Periodic Law is one of the most important ways of making sense of the chemical elements. The Periodic Law states that the chemical elements show repeating, or periodic, patterns if they are arranged according to their atomic number (see page 4). The pattern of elements arranged according to the Periodic Law is called the Periodic Table (see pages 6–7).

The Periodic Table was first described by a Russian teacher, Dmitri Ivanovich Mendeleev, between 1869 and 1870. At that time only 57 elements were known, but he arranged them as a chart (the Periodic Table) on the assumption that there was some order to the elements. He left blank spaces where elements seemed to be missing. Using this chart, he was able to predict, in detail, the chemical and physical proprieties of elements that had not yet been discovered. As soon as scientists looked for the missing elements, using clues provided by Mendeleev's table, they quickly began to find them.

The only element that Mendeleev could not fit into his scheme was hydrogen, so he put it in a box on its own. Otherwise, the elements were all placed in order horizontally. Similarities among the elements can be found by reading up and down the table. These columns are the groups. Each of the rows is a period.

There are eight numbered groups or columns of elements in the Periodic Table. The number of the group represents the number of electrons in the outer shell of the atom. For example, neon and argon have eight electrons in their outer shell and so belong to what can be numbered group 8. However, since helium (with a stable outer shell of only 2 electrons in this exceptional case) is included in this group

The Periodic Table

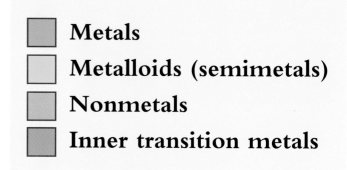

	Metals
	Metalloids (semimetals)
	Nonmetals
	Inner transition metals

GROUPS ▶

PERIODS ▼

	1 (1)	2 (2)	Transition metals (3)	(4)	(5)	(6)	(7)	(8)
1	1 **H** Hydrogen 1							
2	3 **Li** Lithium 7	4 **Be** Beryllium 9						
3	11 **Na** Sodium 23	12 **Mg** Magnesium 24						
4	19 **K** Potassium 39	20 **Ca** Calcium 40	21 **Sc** Scandium 45	22 **Ti** Titanium 48	23 **V** Vanadium 51	24 **Cr** Chromium 52	25 **Mn** Manganese 55	26 **Fe** Iron 56
5	37 **Rb** Rubidium 85	38 **Sr** Strontium 88	39 **Y** Yttrium 89	40 **Zr** Zirconium 91	41 **Nb** Niobium 93	42 **Mo** Molybdenum 96	43 **Tc** Technetium (99)	44 **Ru** Ruthenium 101
6	55 **Cs** Cesium 133	56 **Ba** Barium 137	71 **Lu** Lutetium 175	72 **Hf** Hafnium 178	73 **Ta** Tantalum 181	74 **W** Tungsten 184	75 **Re** Rhenium 186	76 **Os** Osmium 190
7	87 **Fr** Francium (223)	88 **Ra** Radium (226)	103 **Lr** Lawrencium (260)	104 **Rf** Rutherfordium (261)	105 **Db** Dubnium (262)	106 **Sg** Seaborgium (263)	107 **Bh** Bohrium (262)	108 **Hs** Hassium (265)

Lanthanide series	57 **La** Lanthanum 139	58 **Ce** Cerium 140	59 **Pr** Praseodymium 141	60 **Nd** Neodymium 144
Actinide series	89 **Ac** Actinium (227)	90 **Th** Thorium (232)	91 **Pa** Protactinium (231)	92 **U** Uranium (238)

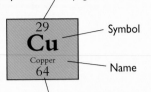

Atomic (proton) number (equivalent to number of electrons). For an explanation see page 4.

29
Cu
Copper
64

Symbol

Name

Approximate relative atomic mass (approximate atomic weight). Those in parentheses are radioactive.

RELATIVE ATOMIC MASS

Chemists used to compare the mass of an atom of an element with that of hydrogen. Hydrogen has one proton and one electron, and is the lightest of atoms, so the mass of other elements could be given relative to hydrogen: mass of one atom of element ÷ mass of one atom of hydrogen. Nowadays, for accuracy, they compare the mass with that of carbon: mass of one atom of element ÷ mass of $\frac{1}{12}$ atom of carbon, and the $^{12}_{6}C$ isotope is used. The relative atomic mass of iodine, for example, is 127. This means that an atom of iodine is 127 times as heavy as one atom of hydrogen or $\frac{1}{12}$ atom of carbon.

The figures used in this book are approximate and so are correctly referred to as the approximate relative atomic mass (the old term used was atomic weight). They are shown underneath the name of each element in the Periodic Table.

				3	4	5	6	7	8 or 0
(9)	(10)	(11)	(12)	(13)	(14)	(15)	(16)	(17)	(18)
									2 **He** Helium 4
				5 **B** Boron 11	6 **C** Carbon 12	7 **N** Nitrogen 14	8 **O** Oxygen 16	9 **F** Fluorine 19	10 **Ne** Neon 20
				13 **Al** Aluminum 27	14 **Si** Silicon 28	15 **P** Phosphorus 31	16 **S** Sulfur 32	17 **Cl** Chlorine 35	18 **Ar** Argon 40
27 **Co** Cobalt 59	28 **Ni** Nickel 59	29 **Cu** Copper 64	30 **Zn** Zinc 65	31 **Ga** Gallium 70	32 **Ge** Germanium 73	33 **As** Arsenic 75	34 **Se** Selenium 79	35 **Br** Bromine 80	36 **Kr** Krypton 84
45 **Rh** Rhodium 103	46 **Pd** Palladium 106	47 **Ag** Silver 108	48 **Cd** Cadmium 112	49 **In** Indium 115	50 **Sn** Tin 119	51 **Sb** Antimony 122	52 **Te** Tellurium 128	53 **I** Iodine 127	54 **Xe** Xenon 131
77 **Ir** Iridium 192	78 **Pt** Platinum 195	79 **Au** Gold 197	80 **Hg** Mercury 201	81 **Tl** Thallium 204	82 **Pb** Lead 207	83 **Bi** Bismuth 209	84 **Po** Polonium (209)	85 **At** Astatine (210)	86 **Rn** Radon (222)
109 **Mt** Meitnerium (266)	110 **Uun** Ununnilium (272)	111 **Uuu** Unununium (272)	112 **Uub** Ununbium (277)		114 **Uuq** Ununquadium (289)		116 **Uuh** Ununhexium (289)		118 **Uuo** Ununoctium (293)

61 **Pm** Promethium (145)	62 **Sm** Samarium 150	63 **Eu** Europium 152	64 **Gd** Gadolinium 157	65 **Tb** Terbium 159	66 **Dy** Dysprosium 163	67 **Ho** Holmium 165	68 **Er** Erbium 167	69 **Tm** Thulium 169	70 **Yb** Ytterbium 173
93 **Np** Neptunium (237)	94 **Pu** Plutonium (244)	95 **Am** Americium (243)	96 **Cm** Curium (247)	97 **Bk** Berkelium (247)	98 **Cf** Californium (251)	99 **Es** Einsteinium (252)	100 **Fm** Fermium (257)	101 **Md** Mendelevium (258)	102 **No** Nobelium (259)

of inert gases, it is often designated group 0 (since that is the number of electrons in the shell outside the stable shell of helium, which is 2, or of neon, argon, krypton, xenon, and radon, which is 8). Sodium and potassium have only 1 electron in their outer shell (outside the stable inner shell of 8 electrons) and so are in group 1.

Transition elements

When atoms have reached a certain complexity (atomic number 21), 10 more electrons can be accommodated in an inner shell. They correspond to the elements scandium to zinc and are called the transition elements. All of the transition elements are metals. They include most of the metals that have the greatest use. They include iron, copper, gold, nickel, and silver. These elements have high melting points and high densities. Most can be alloyed (mixed) together to make materials with new and useful properties.

At lanthanum a further 14 electrons can be included inside the atomic structure, giving rise to the lanthanide series of inner transition metals. (The actual electron configuration is shown in the shell diagram for each element found on its page.)

Alternative grouping system

A recent method of numbering the groups of the Periodic Table that scientists have devised to refer to the transition metals more specifically in the Periodic Table uses the numbers 1 to 18 (shown in parentheses in the table on pages 6–7). In the key facts given for each element these numbers are also shown in parentheses—

▼ Dmitri Ivanovich Mendeleev (1834–1907) was born in Siberia but moved to St. Petersburg to get his university degrees. He was professor of chemistry there from 1867.

for example, for chromium: Position in Periodic Table: transition metal, group (6) (chromium group); period 4.

In the text only the older group numbers shown on the Periodic Table are used.

Radioactive elements are different from all other elements because they lose particles from the nucleus of their atoms (which is called decaying). As a result, over time a radioactive element will change its atomic number and turn into a different element. So, for example, uranium decays to lead. This is shown in equations by numbers before the chemical symbol (example $^{293}_{118}$ Uuo).

Metals, metalloids, and nonmetals

The Periodic Table (pages 6-7) shows a distinct clustering between elements that are metals (colored orange)—and that have a metallic luster and are good electrical and thermal conductors—and the nonmetals (colored purple)—which do not have a luster and are electrical and thermal insulators. Metals form oxides that are basic and so react with acids to produce salts. Nonmetals form oxides that react with water to form acids.

Between these major clusters lie elements known as the metalloids, semimetals, or semiconductors. They are colored yellow. Metalloids are unusual in that they are better conductors at high temperatures (the reverse of metals) and conduct electricity much less than metals but more than nonmetals.

▼ This demonstration shows that transition metals, such as cobalt, make good catalysts.

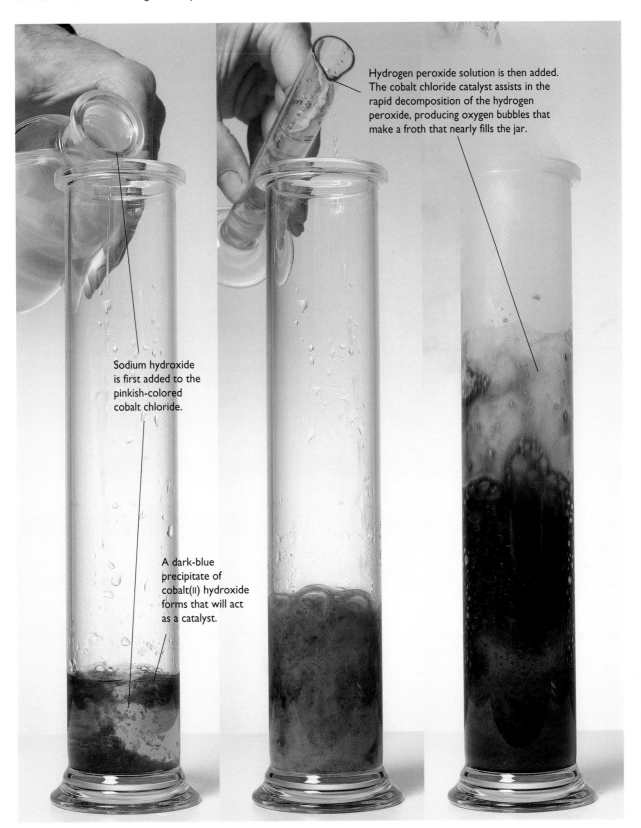

Sodium hydroxide is first added to the pinkish-colored cobalt chloride.

A dark-blue precipitate of cobalt(II) hydroxide forms that will act as a catalyst.

Hydrogen peroxide solution is then added. The cobalt chloride catalyst assists in the rapid decomposition of the hydrogen peroxide, producing oxygen bubbles that make a froth that nearly fills the jar.

Native elements

An element is described as "native" if it occurs in the Earth's crust in an uncombined state as the element itself (elemental state) rather than as a compound. To exist in a native state, an element must be relatively unreactive.

There are some eighteen native elements, none of which is very common. Of the metals, native gold, silver, copper, tin, and platinum are the most commonly found and can be mined as ores.

▼ Graphite is one of two forms of native or elemental carbon.

▼ Diamond is one of two forms of native or elemental carbon. This piece of Kimberlite rock shows the way that most diamond occurs, as a dull yellowish mineral set in a rock background. Only occasionally does a transparent and flawless piece of mineral occur. The cut diamond placed on the rock shows the comparison.

▼ This diagram represents the structure of graphite. It is made only of carbon minerals and is, like diamond, an unreactive substance. However, because the structure is in sheets, the bonds between the sheets are relatively weak, so that when pressure is applied, parts of the mineral flake off. That is what allows graphite to be used in pencils.

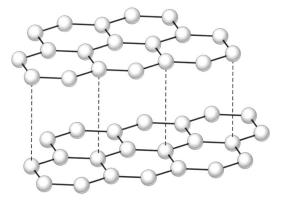

▶ This diagram represents the structure of diamond. It is built of interlocking carbon atoms with no room for other atoms to form part of the structure. That is what makes the mineral so unreactive.

▼ Radon gas is an elemental gas and radioactive. Radon gas is most concentrated over igneous rocks such as granite (below). Overall, radon contributes about 32% of the background radiation we experience.

A sample from a hydrothermal deposit with elemental copper among quartz.

shell, and so it is one electron short of a stable set. That is why it is very reactive. Sodium is also reactive because it contains just one electron more than a stable set. When sodium and chlorine combine, or bond together, they therefore are able to transfer electrons to make both shells stable. That is why it is very difficult to separate sodium and chlorine from common salt (sodium chloride).

Elemental gases

There are several elements that also occur naturally in the uncombined state as gases. They include nitrogen, which is the most abundant gas in the atmosphere, oxygen, and the particularly unreactive noble gases such as argon, neon, and radon.

Compounds and mixtures

A compound is a single substance made of two or more different elements joined together by links called bonds.

Atoms can form compounds by sharing some of the electrons in their outer shells. When atoms do this, they are said to be bonded together.

Atoms of the noble gases, such as helium and argon, have the most stable number of electrons in their outer shells, so these electrons are not easily available—that is why they are unreactive. In contrast, atoms of elements without the most stable set of electrons in their outer shell are reactive. Chlorine, for example, contains only seven electrons in its outer

▲ Chlorine reacts violently with sodium to produce sodium chloride.

▶ Colorless silver nitrate solution is added to colorless potassium iodide solution, producing a new yellow compound of silver iodide.

A compound has a fixed chemical composition. For example, the compound, water always has twice as many hydrogen atoms in it as oxygen atoms. So, the formula for water is H_2O. A mixture, on the other hand, contains more than one substance in no fixed proportion and so cannot be given a chemical formula. Unlike mixtures, the elements that make up a compound are difficult to separate.

Compounds do not inherit the properties of the elements from which they are made. The properties of the liquid water (H_2O), for example, are quite unlike the properties of the elements hydrogen and oxygen (both of which are gases at room temperature). However, all compounds have their own set of properties, such as the temperature at which they melt or boil.

When a compound is formed, energy is usually given out or taken in as heat. When a mixture is formed, no heat is given out or taken in.

The cubic crystals are iron pyrites, a form of iron sulfide.

The transparent crystals are quartz (a form of silica, or silicon oxide)

The black mineral is sphalerite (a form of zinc sulfide).

Carbonates, such as limestone, have been layed down as thick deposits all over the Earth.

Compounds formed from the more reactive elements such as lithium are more stable than compounds of less reactive elements such as mercury. Very reactive elements, such as chlorine and sodium, form compounds with strong bonds that are difficult to break, and so the resulting compounds are exceptionally stable.

Naming compounds

Compounds ending in –ide contain two elements (iron (II) sulfide, for example, is a compound of iron and sulfur: FeS). Compounds ending in –ite or –ate contain oxygen. There is a greater proportion of oxygen in the compounds ending in –ate. Sodium nitrite ($NaNO_2$) and sodium nitrate (Na_2NO_3) are compounds of sodium and nitrogen with different proportions of oxygen.

The occurrence of compounds

Of all the known compounds on Earth, 95% contain carbon and are mainly called organic compounds. However, carbon compounds are not the most abundant in the universe. Instead, compounds that lack carbon (and are called inorganic compounds) form the bulk of the universe. These substances are most of the minerals that make up rocks, most of the air, and water.

The most reactive elements are the alkali metals in Group 1, at the left-hand side of the Periodic Table (see pages 6–7), along with

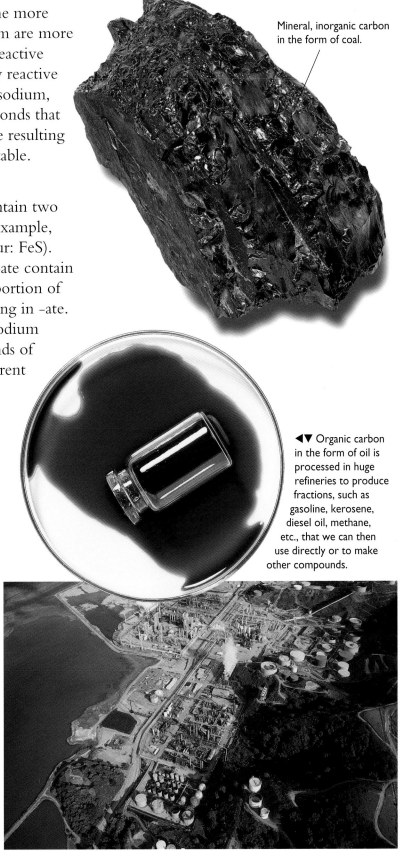

Mineral, inorganic carbon in the form of coal.

◀▼ Organic carbon in the form of oil is processed in huge refineries to produce fractions, such as gasoline, kerosene, diesel oil, methane, etc., that we can then use directly or to make other compounds.

nonmetals such as the halogens (e.g., chlorine), sulfur, and oxygen in Groups 6 and 7 toward the right of the Periodic Table. As a result, many of the compounds found on Earth contain these elements as metal oxides, sulfides, sulfates, and chlorides.

Carbon is a very common element, found both in organic compounds and also in an inorganic form called carbonate.

Obtaining elements from their compounds

There are many ways of obtaining elements from their compounds. Compounds can be broken down with heat in a process called thermal decomposition or by applying electricity in a process called electrolysis.

Compounds can also be broken down through chemical reduction (taking away oxygen). Each method is widely used because the majority of the world's metals are found as compounds, usually chlorides, sulfides, oxides, and carbonates.

All of the less reactive metals form mainly sulfide ores that will not dissolve (they are insoluble). On the other hand, many of the highly reactive metals form chloride compounds that are very soluble, for example, NaCl, sodium chloride, or common salt. Common salt is found dissolved in relatively low concentration in all the world's freshwater lakes and rivers as well as in much greater concentration in the sea. Soluble compounds can be extracted directly by dissolving them, usually in hot water.

▼ The electrolysis of brine to manufacture sodium hydroxide. Chlorine and hydrogen are also produced.

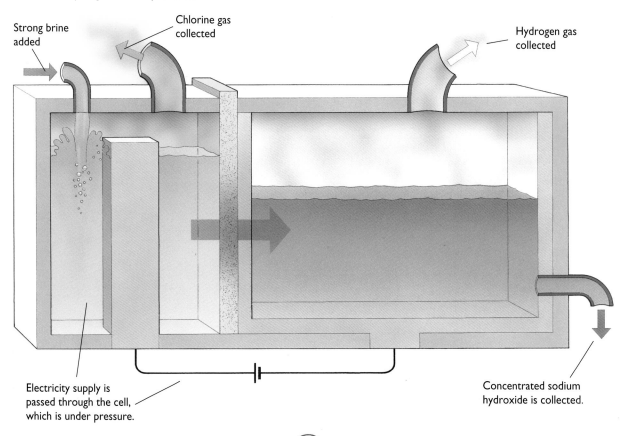

Strong brine added

Chlorine gas collected

Hydrogen gas collected

Electricity supply is passed through the cell, which is under pressure.

Concentrated sodium hydroxide is collected.

Notes on Key Facts

The key facts, such as the example given below for cobalt, present a summary of the information on each element. They appear in a form that allows direct comparisons between elements.

> **Key facts...**
> **Name:** cobalt
> **Symbol:** Co
> **Atomic number:** 27
> **Atomic weight:** 58.93
> **Position in Periodic Table:** transition metal, group (9) (cobalt group); period 4
> **State at room temperature:** solid
> **Color:** lustrous, metallic gray
> **Density of solid:** 8.9 g/cc
> **Melting point:** 1,495°C
> **Boiling point:** 2,870°C
> **Origin of name:** from the German word *kobald*, meaning goblin
> **Shell pattern of electrons:** 2–8–15–2

Name
The name generally accepted. Some of the most recently discovered elements may not have internationally agreed names. Detail about the variation in the names is provided in the section of the page headed Discovery. Names beginning with Un– are intentionally temporary names that will be changed once international agreement on them has been obtained.

Symbol
This is the chemical symbol for the element. For those whose name has not been agreed, the chemical symbol can be expected to change when a final name is assigned to the element.

Atomic number
The number of a chemical element based on the number of protons in the nucleus. The number of protons always equals the number of electrons in the atom.

For example, an atom of actinium has 89 protons in its nucleus, so its atomic number is 89. This number can also be obtained by adding the electrons in the shell diagram. In the case of actinium this is 2–8–18–32–18–9–2 = 89.

Atomic weight
The ratio of the average mass of a chemical element's atoms to one-twelfth the mass of an atom of carbon-12.

Most chemical reactions take place between atoms. Because it is impossible to count the atoms directly, the reactants and products are weighed, and calculations are based on atomic weights. Experimentally determining the atomic weights of the elements was one of the most important achievements of chemists.

Position in Periodic Table
The location of the element in the Periodic Table given on pages 6–7 of this book.

State at room temperature
Whether it is a solid, liquid, or gas.

Color
The commonly observed color of the pure element before it has had a chance to react with its surroundings. Some elements react almost instantaneously with their

surroundings. Thus the color given here and the color most commonly observed (due to oxidation and so on) may differ.

Density

A comparison of the densities of the gases can be done using a simple calculation based on the idea that 24 liters of any gas at room temperature and standard pressure will have a mass in grams equal to its molecular weight. Most gaseous elements exist as diatomic molecules, for example, O_2, N_2, and so on.

Examples:
Oxygen (atomic weight 16)
Molecular weight of $O_2 = 2 \times 16 = 32$
Thus density = 32/24 = 1.3g/l

Hydrogen (atomic weight 1)
Molecular weight of $H_2 = 2 \times 1 = 2$
Thus density = 2/14 = 0.083g/l

The noble gases exist as single atoms.
Helium (atomic weight 4)
Molecular weight of He = 4
Thus density = 4/24 = 0.17g/l

Melting point/Boiling point

Because of the difficulty in obtaining absolutely pure samples of some elements, the unstable nature of some elements, and the difficulties in taking the measurements at high temperatures, variations can be found between sets of published data. The values given in the key facts of these books are typical quoted values from established scientific institutions.

Origin of name

The derivation of the name is given. The main text may explain this derivation more fully.

Shell pattern of electrons

Electrons move in certain places around the nucleus. These places are known as shells. The shell pattern is thus the pattern of electrons that surround the nucleus of an atom. The list is given from the center outward. The shell pattern corresponds to the shell diagram given on each page.

Shell diagrams

The shell diagrams, such as the ones shown below, are color-coded to match the Periodic Table on pages 6-7. Hydrogen and other nonmetals are colored purple. Metals are orange, with the actinide and lanthanide series green. Metalloids (semimetals) are coded yellow.

Actinium (Ac)

Element 89. It is a radioactive element in the actinide series on the Periodic Table.

This rare, silvery-white metal glows blue in the dark. Actinium is one of the decay products of uranium, decaying further to thorium-227 and radium-223. Actinium is chemically similar to other rare earths, particularly lanthanum. Actinium is 150 times more radioactive than radium and is an important element for the production of neutrons.

Discovery

Actinium was discovered in 1899 by André-Louis Debierne while he was trying to find ways to separate rare oxides. It was isolated independently in 1902 by F. Giesel.

Technology

It is a powerful source of alpha rays. As a highly radioactive element, it has limited uses. Actinium is, however, a concentrated form of radioactivity and is used in nuclear power plants and as a source of neutrons in physics experiments.

Geology

Actinium is found together with uranium in ores such as pitchblende. It appears in extremely small amounts even in its natural ores, there being less than a ten-millionth part of actinium in pitchblende.

Key facts...
Name: actinium
Symbol: Ac
Atomic number: 89
Atomic weight: 227
Position in Periodic Table: inner transition metal; period 7 (actinide series)
State at room temperature: solid
Color: silvery-white
Density of solid: 10.07 g/cc
Melting point: 1,050°C
Boiling point: 3,200°C
Origin of name: from the Greek word *aktinos*, meaning ray
Shell pattern of electrons: 2–8–18–32–18–9–2

Biology

Actinium is not found naturally in living things. Its low concentration in nature means that it is never naturally a health hazard. However, its radioactivity makes it highly dangerous in concentrated form.

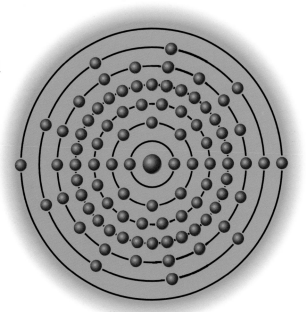

Aluminum (Al)

Element 13. Aluminum is a lightweight, silvery-white metal. It belongs to group 3 (the boron group) on the Periodic Table.

Aluminum is the most common metallic element in the Earth's crust. It is the third most abundant element on Earth after oxygen and silicon.

It is reactive and is never found as the native metal. It mainly occurs as aluminum oxide.

Aluminum is the most widely used nonferrous metal. It is nonmagnetic and easily worked. However, it was initially so difficult to obtain from its ore that it was very expensive and so was regarded as a precious metal. Only when electric power became available and it could be more easily refined did its price drop. At the same time, it found many new uses. By the 1960s aluminum became the most commonly used nonferrous metal.

It is refined using the Bayer process.

Aluminum is weak and soft in pure form, but is easily alloyed with other metals; then it is transformed into a hard, strong, lightweight material. Copper, magnesium, silicon, and manganese are all used as alloying metals.

Key facts...

Name: aluminum
Symbol: Al
Atomic number: 13
Atomic weight: 26.98
Position in Periodic Table: group 3 (13) (boron group); period 3
State at room temperature: solid
Color: silvery-white
Density of solid: 2.7 g/cc
Melting point: 660.32°C
Boiling point: 2,519°C
Origin of name: from the Latin word *alumen*, meaning alum, a compound of aluminum used in fixing dyes

The name *alumine* was first proposed in 1761 by de Morveau. Davy suggested alumium in 1807 and then agreed to change it to aluminum. Scientists then agreed to change the ending to "ium" to be in line with scientific notation for the newly discovered elements. Aluminium remains the official international scientific spelling. However, in 1925 the American Chemical Society decided to revert to aluminum, which is why there are two spellings for this element.

Shell pattern of electrons: 2–8–3

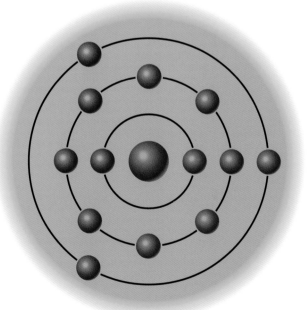

For more on aluminum, see Volume 7: Aluminum in the *Elements* set.

Discovery

It was discovered in 1825 by Hans Christian Oersted in Denmark. He reacted aluminum chloride ($AlCl_3$) with a potassium amalgam (an alloy of potassium and mercury). It formed an aluminum amalgam (and potassium chloride). By heating the aluminum amalgam, the mercury boiled off, and aluminum was left.

Technology

Alum was used by ancient civilizations for stabilizing dyes (alum is a mordant). Aluminum metal is now used as a packaging material (cooking foil, soft drink cans, and so on), for window frames, and cooking pans (often with a nonstick inner surface). It is widely applied in the building industry as a structural material where lightness and resistance to corrosion are important. It also appears in high-tension electricity cables because it is much lighter and cheaper than copper (an even better conductor). Aluminum is used for lightness in engines, aircraft, and spacecraft. Aluminum can be evaporated in a vacuum and then can coat other substances, making a decorative and corrosion-resistant surface. It is a good reflector of radiant heat.

Geology

Aluminum makes up about 8% by weight of the Earth's crust. It is found in most minerals. However, it is only commercially mined from its hydrated oxide, the mineral bauxite ($Al_2O_3.2H_2O$). This soft subsurface material occurs in tropical soils together with iron oxides. When hardened in a soil, such material is called laterite.

Some oxides of aluminum are precious stones (gemstones), such as ruby (red) and sapphire (blue), as well as hard abrasive materials such as emery and corundum.

Aluminum is found in most soils as part of the clay minerals.

Biology

Aluminum compounds are not an essential part of living things; and although not harmful in small quantities, aluminum can be toxic if taken in over a long period of time. The use of aluminum pans (with no nonstick liner) may be one way in which people can ingest aluminum, which builds up in the body. Alzheimer's disease may be a disease linked to aluminum poisoning.

Acid rain mobilizes aluminum compounds in the soil. They then are absorbed by plant roots and taken into the plants, where they cause death. The acid rain/aluminum relationship is the main result of acid rain.

Aluminum is highly reflective and is cheaper to produce than many other similar metals. As a result, it can be used on a large scale, such as in the mirrors of this solar generating plant.

Rubies are prized gemstones. They are made mainly of aluminum and oxygen (aluminum oxide).

Antimony (Sb)

Element 51. Antimony, a metalloid in group 5 (the nitrogen group) on the Periodic Table, gets its symbol from the Latin for tin, *stibium*.

It is a silvery, bluish-white solid, which is very brittle and has a flaky texture.

It is found as a gray sulfide mineral called stibnite. Antimony is a poor conductor of heat and electricity, and tarnishes only slightly in air, more in moist air. When it is heated in air, it burns with a brilliant blue flame and gives out white fumes. It has no uses as a pure element; but when alloyed with metals, it makes the alloy hard and strong.

Discovery

Antimony has been known since ancient times.

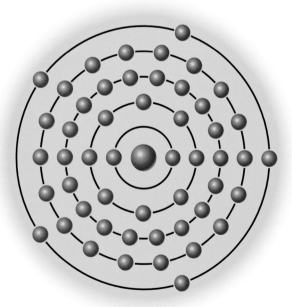

Key facts...
Name: antimony
Symbol: Sb
Atomic number: 51
Atomic weight: 121.75
Position in Periodic Table: group 5 (15) (nitrogen group); period 5
State at room temperature: solid
Color: bluish-white
Density of solid: 6.69 g/cc
Melting point: 630°C
Boiling point: 1,380°C
Origin of name: from the Greek words *anti* + *monos*, meaning not alone. The symbol Sb comes from the Latin word *stibium*, meaning tin.
Shell pattern of electrons: 2–8–18–18–5

Technology

Antimony is obtained by heating the sulfide with iron. The sulfide reacts with the iron to leave the element antimony. The earliest use of antimony was as black eye makeup. It is now used as a doping compound in semiconductors and as an alloy to harden lead. In this way it appears in bullets and armor for electrical cables. The alloy also has low friction qualities. Many compounds are used in flame-proofing and in paints, glass, and ceramics.

Geology

Native antimony is occasionally found. However, most antimony occurs in the mineral form. The main minerals of antimony are the sulfides stibnite (Sb_2S_3) and ullmanite (NiSbS).

Biology

Antimony and its compounds are toxic, causing liver damage. They are also an irritant to the skin. In the past antimony compounds have been used as medicines, but their highly poisonous character means they were of dubious value.

Americium (Am)

Element 95. It is an artificial, radioactive rare earth in the actinide series on the Periodic Table.

It is also called a transuranium element because it has a higher atomic number than uranium. It is made from plutonium in a nuclear reactor.

The metal is silvery-white. It is not very reactive and tarnishes only slowly in air. It is about three times as radioactive as radium.

Key facts...

Name: americium
Symbol: Am
Atomic number: 95
Atomic weight: 243
Position in Periodic Table: inner transition metal; period 7 (actinide series)
State at room temperature: solid
Color: silvery-white
Density of solid: 13.7 g/cc
Melting point: 994°C
Boiling point: 2,600°C
Origin of name: it was named for America.
Shell pattern of electrons: 2–8–18–32–25–8–2

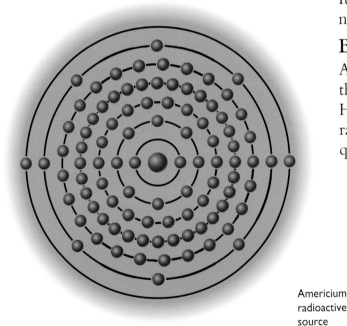

Geology

It is not present in rocks because it does not occur naturally.

Biology

Americium is radioactive and so can theoretically be dangerous to health. However, because it is not highly radioactive, it is safe to use in the tiny quantities needed for smoke detection.

Americium radioactive source

Discovery

It was discovered in the United States by Glenn Seaborg, Ralph James, L. Morgan, and Albert Ghiorso in 1944 during experiments in a nuclear reactor.

Technology

Americium is the radioactive source in smoke detectors. It is also used where portable gamma rays are needed for scientific purposes.

Argon (Ar)

Element 18. An inert (unreactive) gas and the most abundant member in group 0 (the noble gases) on the Periodic Table. It is not known to form any true compounds.

It is colorless, odorless, and tasteless.

Argon is heavier than air. When electricity is passed through argon, the argon glows pale red. The fact that the atmosphere of Mars contains argon was discovered because argon's characteristic color could be detected by special telescopes.

Discovery

Argon was isolated from air in 1894 in Scotland by Lord Rayleigh and Sir William Ramsay. When they had removed nitrogen, oxygen, carbon dioxide, and water from liquid air, argon was left.

Technology

Argon is used in light bulbs and in other places where an unreactive gas is needed, for example, in the manufacture of silicon chips, where an oxygen-free environment is essential. Argon is obtained as a by-product of the liquefaction of air.

Geology

Argon makes up about 1.3% of the atmosphere by weight and 0.94% by volume.

Biology

Argon is not an active substance in living things.

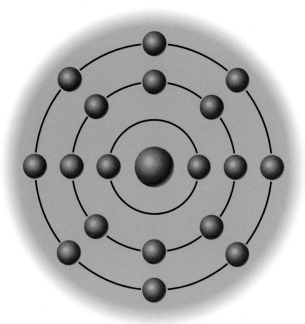

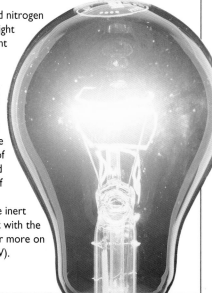

▶ A mixture of argon and nitrogen is used in incandescent light bulbs. When the filament gets hot, it sends out atoms into the bulb. If the bulb contained a reactive gas, the life of the filament would be reduced, and a thin film of metal atoms would be deposited on the inside of the bulb, blackening it and reducing the brightness of the light.

Argon and nitrogen are inert gases and so do not react with the intensely hot filament. For more on filaments, *see* tungsten (W).

For more on argon, see Volume 1: Hydrogen and the Noble Gases in the *Elements* set.

Arsenic (As)

Element 33. A metalloid in group 5 (the nitrogen group) on the Periodic Table.

It is common in nature as compounds and occasionally in gray and yellow elemental form. Gray arsenic is very brittle and rapidly tarnishes in air; the yellow form is softer.

Arsenic sublimes, changing from solid to vapor and back to solid again without the intervening liquid phase. Arsenic is well known as a poison. The smell of arsenic vapor resembles garlic.

Discovery

Arsenic has been known since ancient times. It was mined by all ancient civilizations, probably for use as a poison.

Technology

Arsenic oxide is used as a pesticide (poison), in adhesives, and as a decolorizer in glassmaking. It is also used in the doping of silicon in making integrated circuits. It can be used to make lead shot harder and also in fireworks to produce color.

Geology

The native form of arsenic only appears very occasionally. It is most usually found as a sulfide—realgar (As_4S_4), orpiment (As_2S_3)—or as the oxide arsenolite (As_2O_3), and in iron sulfide minerals such as mispickel or arsenpyrite (FeAsS).

Key facts...
Name: arsenic
Symbol: As
Atomic number: 33
Atomic weight: 74.92
Position in Periodic Table: group 5 (15) (nitrogen group); period 4
State at room temperature: solid
Color: metallic gray or yellow
Density of solid: 5.7 g/cc
Melting point: 817°C
Boiling point: n/a
Origin of name: from the Greek word *arsenikon*, meaning yellow orpiment
Shell pattern of electrons: 2–8–18–5

Biology

Although arsenic is poisonous to both plants and animals in large doses, it is an essential microelement for some algae and in many animals. Without trace amounts of arsenic growth is stunted.

◄ Bright yellow orpiment crystals with red realgar veins. Both minerals contain arsenic.

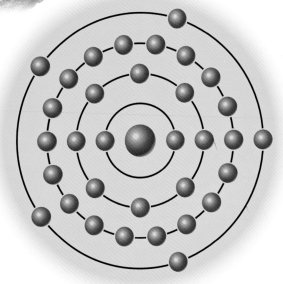

Astatine (At)

Element 85. It is a radioactive halogen element and is the heaviest member in group 7 on the Periodic Table. The longest half-life of astatine is 8.3 hours. As a result, it decays extremely quickly. It is made in nuclear reactors.

Discovery

It was discovered during experiments in a nuclear reactor by Dale R. Corson, K. R. MacKenzie, and Emilio Segrè at the University of California in 1940 by bombarding bismuth with alpha particles.

Technology

It has no uses.

Geology

It does not occur naturally except as part of the decay of uranium and thorium minerals.

Key facts...
Name: astatine
Symbol: At
Atomic number: 85
Atomic weight: 210
Position in Periodic Table: group 7 (17) (halogens); period 6
State at room temperature: solid
Color: metallic
Density: n/a
Melting point: 337°C
Boiling point: n/a
Origin of name: from the Greek word *astatos*, meaning unstable because of its short half-life.
Shell pattern of electrons: 2–8–18–32–18–7

Biology

As a radioactive halogen it is theoretically harmful but is produced in tiny quantities.

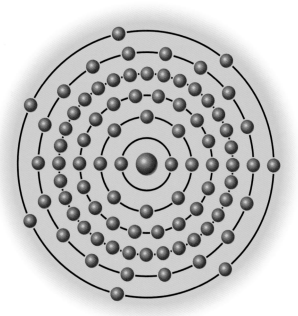

The mineral barite is made of barium sulfate.

Barium (Ba)

Element 56. It is one of the alkaline earth metals in group 2 on the Periodic Table.

It is silvery-white, leadlike element when freshly cut but slightly heavier than lead. The metal reacts with air quickly and tarnishes rapidly. It is very reactive with water and alcohol.

Barium is isolated by electrolysis of molten barium chloride. Barium collects at the cathode.

Key facts...

Name: barium
Symbol: Ba
Atomic number: 56
Atomic weight: 137.34
Position in Periodic Table: group 2 (2) (alkaline earth metal); period 6
State at room temperature: solid
Color: silvery-white
Density of solid: 3.51 g/cc
Melting point: 725°C
Boiling point: 1,640°C
Origin of name: from the Greek word *barys*, meaning heavy
Shell pattern of electrons: 2–8–18–18–8–2

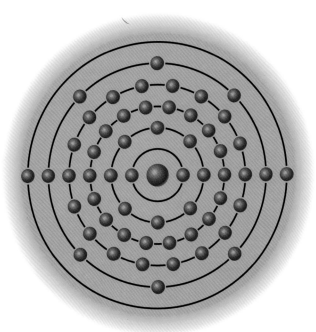

▼ Brown–green barium flame

Barium sulfate makes a white filler for rubber and paper. It also helps make a brilliant white coloring substance for paint. Barium is used in glassmaking. Barium nitrate makes the green color in signal flares and in fireworks. Barium carbonate is a rodent poison.

Geology

Barium is too reactive to form native deposits. It is mainly found as the mineral barite. Barite is easily distinguished from other white minerals by its weight.

Biology

Barium is not normally a part of living things. Barium sulfate is insoluble and so can be used for tracing purposes in medicine (x-rays can trace a "barium meal"). Other barium compounds are poisonous.

Discovery

Barium was discovered in England in 1808 by Sir Humphry Davy by electrolysis of a molten barium oxide.

Technology

The element is used in metallurgy, and its compounds appear in fireworks, petroleum mining, and radiology.

Berkelium (Bk)

Element 97. It is an artificial element in the actinide series on the Periodic Table.

All of the isotopes of berkelium are radioactive. No one has ever seen metallic berkelium, but it is expected to be a silvery metal similar to others in the actinide series.

At present relatively little is known about this element.

Key facts...

Name: berkelium
Symbol: Bk
Atomic number: 97
Atomic weight: 247
Position in Periodic Table: inner transition metal; period 7 (actinide series)
State at room temperature: solid
Color: unknown
Density of solid: 14.78 g/cc
Melting point: 986°C
Boiling point: n/a
Origin of name: named after the University of California at Berkeley
Shell pattern of electrons: 2–8–18–32–27–8–2

Discovery

It was discovered in 1949 by Stanley Thompson, Albert Ghiorso, and Glenn Seaborg when they bombarded americium with helium ions.

The first pure berkelium compound obtained was berkelium chloride. In 1962 a 3-billionth of a gram was produced.

Technology

Because it has only been isolated in such tiny amounts, it has no uses.

Geology

Because it is an artificial element, it does not occur naturally.

Biology

Since it is an artificial element, it has no biological role.

Beryllium (Be)

Element 4. Beryllium is a brittle, steel-gray metal. It is a poorly reacting element that does not tarnish in air. It is a member of group 2 on the Periodic Table.

Beryl is used to obtain the element beryllium by roasting it with a fluoride compound that makes beryllium fluoride, which is soluble in water. Further treatment makes it precipitate. Beryllium oxide is harder than glass.

Key facts...
Name: beryllium (formerly known as glucinium)
Symbol: Be
Atomic number: 4
Atomic weight: 9.01
Position in Periodic Table: group 2 (2) (alkaline earth metal); period 2
State at room temperature: solid
Color: steel-gray
Density of solid: 1.85 g/cc
Melting point: 1,278°C
Boiling point: 2,970°C
Origin of name: from the Greek word *beryllos*, meaning beryl
Shell pattern of electrons: 2–2

Discovery

Beryllium was discovered by Nicholas Louis Vauquelin in France in 1797. It was only isolated as an element in 1828 by Friederich Wöhler.

Technology

Beryllium is used in metal alloys to add hardness and to prevent sparking. An alloy of 2% beryllium and copper makes a very strong and hard alloy that resists wear and goes into precision bearings. The space shuttle uses beryllium alloys for their lightness and stiffness. It absorbs neutrons and so can be used in nuclear reactors. Some gas mantles are impregnated with beryllium compounds.

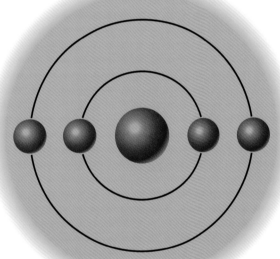

Hexagonal crystal of beryl

Geology

It is found combined in nature as the mineral beryl, beryllium aluminum silicate ($Be_3Al_2(SiO_3)_6$). Gemstones of beryl are emerald and aquamarine.

Biology

Compounds of beryllium are poisonous.

Bismuth (Bi)

Element 83. Bismuth is hard, brittle, and gray-white.

Bismuth is the most metallic of the elements in group 5 (the nitrogen group) on the Periodic Table. It is one of the heavy metals.

It is notable for its low melting point, its ability to become magnetized, its high electrical resistance, and its very low conduction of heat (only mercury conducts less well). Alloys containing more than 55% bismuth expand on freezing.

Discovery

Bismuth has been known since ancient times. It was only identified as an element in its own right in 1740. Today it is mainly obtained as a by-product of the refining of nonferrous metals.

Key facts...

Name: bismuth
Symbol: Bi
Atomic number: 83
Atomic weight: 208.98
Position in Periodic Table: group 5 (15) (nitrogen group); period 6
State at room temperature: solid
Color: gray-white with pinkish tinge
Density of solid: 9.75 g/cc
Melting point: 271.3°C
Boiling point: 1,560°C
Origin of name: from the German word *bisemutum*
Shell pattern of electrons: 2–8–18–32–18–5

Technology

Bismuth is used to make low-melting-point alloys, in solders, and in automatic sprinkler heads (which have to begin working at the earliest signs of a fire). For example, Wood's metal, which is 50% bismuth, 25% lead, 12.5% tin, and 12.5% cadmium, has a melting point as low as 70°C. Bismuth oxide can give a pearly sheen to cast-iron and ceramic products. It is used as a coolant in nuclear reactors because it has a low melting point but a very high boiling point.

Geology

Native bismuth crystals do occur in a number of ores but only in small amounts. The most common ore of bismuth is the oxide called bismite (Bi_2O_3), but most bismuth is obtained as part of the processing of other ores.

Biology

Bismuth is not found naturally in living things. However, traditionally bismuth compounds were used to settle digestive problems and for skin ailments such as eczema. It is also found in hemorrhoid creams. Although it is one of the heavy metals, it is not particularly toxic.

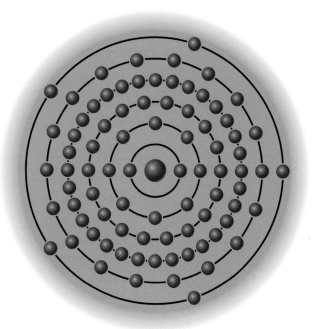

Bohrium (Bh)

Element 107. Has also been known as unnilseptium (Uns) and neilsbohrium (Ns). It is an artificial radioactive element belonging to the transition metals on the Periodic Table.

It was made by fusion of an isotope of lead and chromium. Bohrium decays so rapidly it has never been seen.

Discovery

It was discovered in 1976 at the Joint Institute for Nuclear Research in Dubna, Russia. It was confirmed by Peter Armbruster and Gottfried Münzenber at Darmstadt, Germany, in 1981.

Key facts...

Name: bohrium
Symbol: Bh
Atomic number: 107
Atomic weight: 262
Position in Periodic Table: transition metal, group (7) (manganese group); period 7
State at room temperature: solid
Color: unknown
Density: n/a
Melting point: n/a
Boiling point: n/a
Origin of name: named for Neils Bohr
Shell pattern of electrons: 2–8–18–32–32–13–2

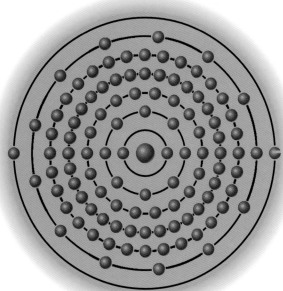

Synthetic bismuth crystals

Technology

Because it has only been isolated in such tiny amounts, it has no uses.

Geology

Because it is an artificial element, it does not occur naturally.

Biology

As an artificial element, it does not occur in living things.

Boron (B)

Element 5. Boron is a metalloid (with properties between a metal and a nonmetal) in group 3 on the Periodic Table. It is close to silicon in its chemistry. For example, it is chemically inert and even resists strong acids. Because it is unreactive, it is difficult to isolate the element from its compounds. It is a very hard, black semiconductor.

Discovery

Boron compounds have been known since ancient times, but the element was only isolated in 1808 independently by Joseph-Louis Gay-Lussac and Louis-Jacques Thenard and also by Sir Humphry Davy. They did it by reacting boric acid with potassium.

Technology

It will scratch corundum (hardness 9 on Mohs' scale of hardness) and so can be used as an abrasive.

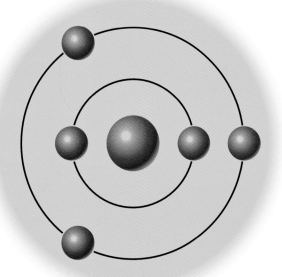

Borosilicate glass bowl

Boron can increase hardness in steel. Borosilicate glass, the common heat-proof glass used for ovenware, is often found under the trade name Pyrex®. Borax is used as a flux in welding and a water-softening agent in some laundry detergents. Boron compounds are used to make enamel. Boron produces a green color in fireworks.

Geology

Boron is not found as a native element. It commonly appears in the minerals borax ($Na_2B_4O_5(OH)_4 \cdot 8H_2O$) and tourmaline.

Biology

Boron is needed by algae and plants. It is probably not essential for animals. Boracic acid is an antiseptic, and in more concentrated form it is applied to control roaches and other insects.

Bromine (Br)

Element 35. Bromine is one of the halogens in group 7 on the Periodic Table. It is the only liquid nonmetallic element. An amber-brown gas, it is highly poisonous.

Discovery

In 1826 the French chemist Antoine-Jérôme Balard discovered bromine as a compound in salt left after the evaporation of seawater. Bromine is still obtained commercially from seawater.

Technology

Bromine compounds (bromides) are common in photography. Bromine is a bleaching agent and is used as a flame retardant, especially for plastics.

Tyrian purple is a dye made from a type of clam in which there is a high concentration of bromine.

Geology

Bromine is not found as a native element but as a bromide in seawater. A small number of minerals also contain the bromide, especially evaporites that were formed by evaporation of seawater.

Biology

Bromine is a trace element in animals; but when present in too much concentration, it causes depression. If inhaled as a vapor, bromine is extremely poisonous, affecting the eyes and throat. It produces sores on the skin. It goes into compounds as a sedative in medicine and as a pesticide against insects. Bromine also helps in water purification.

Key facts...
Name: bromine
Symbol: Br
Atomic number: 35
Atomic weight: 79.9
Position in Periodic Table: group 7 (17) (halogens); period 4
State at room temperature: liquid
Color: amber-brown
Density of liquid: 3.12 g/cc
Melting point: -7.2°C
Boiling point: 59°C
Origin of name: from the Greek word *bromos*, meaning stench
Shell pattern of electrons: 2–8–18–7

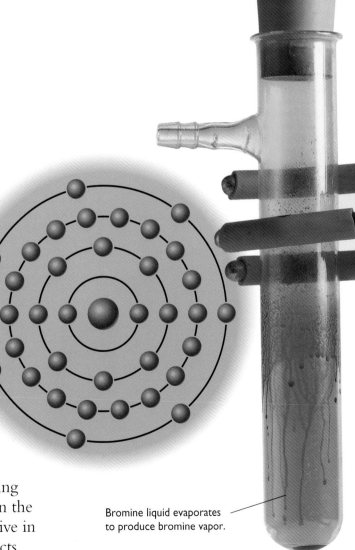

Bromine liquid evaporates to produce bromine vapor.

For more on bromine, see Volume 14: Chlorine, Fluorine, Bromine, and Iodine in the *Elements* set.

Cadmium (Cd)

Element 48. Cadmium is a silvery-white metal in the zinc group (transition metals) on the Periodic Table. Cadmium is a soft metal, easily cut with a knife. It has a low melting point. One unique feature is the way the metal makes a sound like a scream when it is bent.

Discovery

Friedrich Stromeyer, a German chemist, discovered the element in 1817 by extracting cadmium sulfide from an ore containing mostly zinc carbonate.

Technology

Cadmium is obtained as a by-product during the refining of zinc ores. It is used in Ni-Cd (nicad) batteries and for electroplating steel, iron, copper, brass, and in other alloys to protect them from corrosion. Silver solder is made with

> ### Key facts...
> Name: cadmium
> Symbol: Cd
> Atomic number: 48
> Atomic weight: 112.4
> Position in Periodic Table: transition metal, group (12) (zinc group); period 5
> State at room temperature: solid
> Color: silvery-white
> Density of solid: 8.65 g/cc
> Melting point: 321°C
> Boiling point: 765°C
> Origin of name: from the Greek word *kadmeia*, meaning calamine (because cadmium was first found as an impurity in a mineral once called calamine, zinc carbonate. Calamine is now known as smithsonite).
> Shell pattern of electrons: 2–8–18–18–2

cadmium. It goes into some of the phosphors that coat television tubes. Because it absorbs neutrons, cadmium also makes control rods in nuclear reactors. Cadmium compounds also go into pigments. Because cadmium is a very toxic heavy metal, its application is now more restricted.

Geology

Found as small amounts as impurities in zinc ores such as sphalerite (zinc sulfide, ZnS) and smithsonite (zinc carbonate, $ZnCO_3$).

Biology

Highly toxic heavy metal.

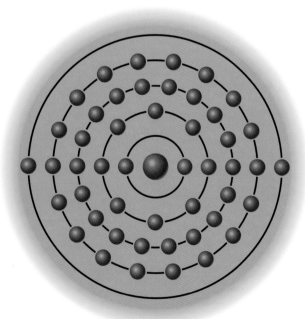

▶ Cadmium is a dense metal that is used to shield nuclear reactors and as the moderating material for the control rods inside the reactor core.

For more on cadmium, see Volume 6: Zinc, Cadmium, and Mercury in the *Elements* set.

Calcium (Ca)

Element 20. Calcium is a hard, silvery alkaline earth metal in group 2 on the Periodic Table. It is the fifth most abundant of the chemical elements in the Earth's crust.

It does not occur as a native metal, but in compounds, of which calcium carbonate (limestone) is the most common. The element reacts with air, burning with a yellow-red flame to form a white nitride coating. It reacts with water, liberating oxygen.

Discovery

It was first isolated by Sir Humphry Davy in 1808. He produced it by electrolysis of a mixture of lime and mercury oxide.

Technology

As calcium oxide (lime), it goes into cement and fertilizer (slaked lime, hydrated calcium oxide, $Ca(OH)_2$). The Romans roasted limestone to produce lime (CaO) and used it to make the first cement (calcium oxide reacts with carbon dioxide in the air and sets as hard calcium carbonate). It was called calx. By 975 calcium sulfate ($CaSO_4$) was used to set bones and became known as plaster of Paris. It can also be a reducing agent for metals.

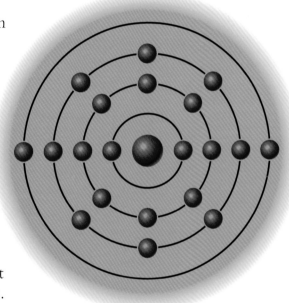

Geology

Calcium does not occur as a native element. It is found as limestone and chalk ($CaCO_3$) and as gypsum ($CaSO_4$) and fluorite (CaF_2). Limestone is one of the world's most common rocks. Because limestone reacts with water and is thereby dissolved, limestones can be eroded

◀ These huge stalagmites in the Big Room, Carlsbad Caverns, New Mexico, are the result of calcium carbonate precipitation over thousands of years.

◀ Whalebone is rich in calcium. This figure of an Inuit hunter is carved from fossilized whalebone. The people of Pangnirtung, Baffin Island, found that the hard texture of fossilized whalebone provided a good alternative to soapstone, the traditional Inuit carving material.

▶ Calcium rapidly reacts with oxygen in the air to form a protective (dull) oxide coating that tends to prevent any further reaction. It only looks silvery when freshly cut.

in unique ways. They include the formation of underground tunnels and caverns and the growth of stalactites and stalagmites. Many limestones are a mixture of the remains of the skeletons of animals and mud. The type of limestone is often named for the most common fossil, for example, shelly limestone for the large number of fossil clam shells found in it.

Biology

Calcium is an essential part of all animal cell walls. It is found in leaves, bones, teeth, and shells, often as calcium phosphate. Calcium helps in blood clotting.

Calcium is harmless, and extra calcium is recommended for people as they become older to help ensure they guard against the risk of bone loss.

▶ (Three pictures to right) If limestone is heated in a furnace, it decomposes to produce white calcium oxide (quicklime). If water is dropped onto the calcium oxide, a vigorous reaction takes place in which heat is given off. The blocks swell and crumble, and the water is turned to steam. The dry powder left behind is calcium hydroxide.

For more on calcium, see Volume 3: Calcium and Magnesium in the *Elements* set.

Californium (Cf)

Element 98. Californium is an artificial metallic radioactive rare-earth element in the actinide series on the Periodic Table.

Discovery

Discovered at the University of California by Glenn T. Seaborg, Stanley G. Thompson, Albert Ghiorso, and Kenneth Street in 1950 by bombarding curium-242 with helium ions.

Technology

It is used as a portable neutron source for the detection of gold or silver and also in moisture gauges for finding water and oil-bearing layers in oil wells.

Geology

Because it is an artificial element, it does not occur naturally.

Biology

It is a radioactive element and so a biological hazard. It is used as a very intense source of neutrons in medicine.

Key facts...
Name: Californium
Symbol: Cf
Atomic number: 98
Atomic weight: 251
Position in Periodic Table: inner transition metal; period 7 (actinide series)
State at room temperature: solid
Color: unknown
Density of solid: 15.1 g/cc
Melting point: 900°C
Boiling point: n/a
Origin of name: named for the state and University of California
Shell pattern of electrons: 2–8–18–32–28–8–2

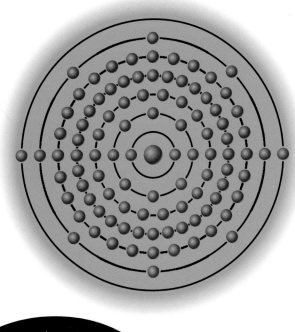

Blocks of quicklime.

The blocks expand and heat up if water is added.

Carbon (C)

Element 6. A nonmetallic element in group 4 on the Periodic Table.

Carbon forms a uniquely large range of compounds. It is found in about 90% of all known compounds, even though it is not especially plentiful. The isotope carbon-12 is used as the standard relative to which the atomic mass of all the other elements is measured. The isotope carbon-14 is radioactive and allows radiocarbon dating.

Carbon makes crystalline diamond and graphite as well as the deposit called carbon black, the result of combustion.

Of the many impure noncrystalline forms of carbon, the most common are coal, coke, and charcoal.

Carbon is found in all living matter.

Carbon group elements—group 4 on the Periodic Table—include carbon, silicon (Si), germanium (Ge), tin (Sn), and lead (Pb).

Discovery

Carbon has been known since ancient times

Technology

Diamond is the hardest natural substance, is transparent, and is regarded as a gemstone. It is also a poor conductor of electricity. It is used as a cutting tool. Graphite is opaque, soft, and conducts electricity very well. Its slippery properties make it useful as a lubricant and as the "lead" in pencils. Coal, coke, and charcoal are fuels. Charcoal also absorbs gases to

Key facts...
Name: carbon
Symbol: C
Atomic number: 6
Atomic weight: 12.01
Position in Periodic Table: group 4 (14) (carbon group); period 2
State at room temperature: solid
Color: graphite is black, diamond is colorless
Density of solid: diamond: 3.52 g/cc; graphite: 2.25 g/cc
Melting point: 3,550°C
Boiling point: 4,827°C
Origin of name: from the Latin word *carbo*, meaning charcoal
Shell pattern of electrons: 2–4

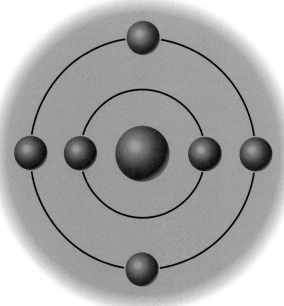

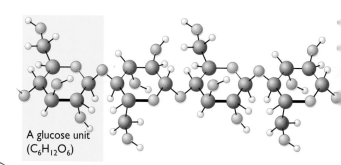

▼ A diagrammatic representation of a section of rayon. The rayon polymer can be made of up to 270 glucose units derived from cellulose.

A glucose unit ($C_6H_{12}O_6$)

remove the color from materials and goes into gunpowder.

Carbon-14, an isotope with a half-life of 5,730 years, helps date organic materials such as archeological specimens.

Geology

Carbon is found in all stars and also in the atmosphere of many planets. Comets also contain carbon. Carbon appears as diamond, graphite, and in a noncrystalline black form (for example, lamp black, soot). It has recently been discovered in a form called buckminsterfullerene. The main location of diamonds is in volcanic pipes. The atmosphere of the Earth is 4% carbon dioxide; on Mars it is 96%. Carbon dioxide is found in all water. It is also found in rocks such as limestone ($CaCO_3$) as well as in all fossil fuel deposits (hydrocarbons).

Biology

Carbon is part of all living matter and is essential to all life. Carbon dioxide is absorbed by plants from the air and used to help make tissues. The carbon is passed on to animals when they eat plant food.

Some compounds of carbon are dangerous, for example, methane, ethane, and cyanide.

▲ Coal is made of carbon and is an important fossil fuel.

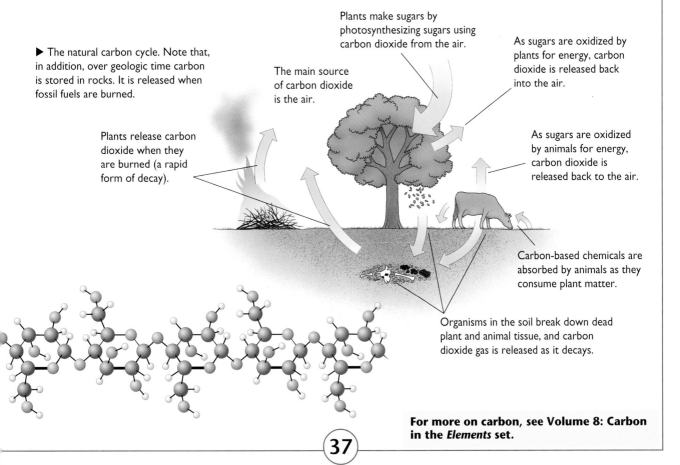

► The natural carbon cycle. Note that, in addition, over geologic time carbon is stored in rocks. It is released when fossil fuels are burned.

Plants make sugars by photosynthesizing sugars using carbon dioxide from the air.

The main source of carbon dioxide is the air.

As sugars are oxidized by plants for energy, carbon dioxide is released back into the air.

As sugars are oxidized by animals for energy, carbon dioxide is released back to the air.

Plants release carbon dioxide when they are burned (a rapid form of decay).

Carbon-based chemicals are absorbed by animals as they consume plant matter.

Organisms in the soil break down dead plant and animal tissue, and carbon dioxide gas is released as it decays.

For more on carbon, see Volume 8: Carbon in the *Elements* set.

Cerium (Ce)

Element 58. Cerium is one of the rare-earth metals (lanthanides) on the Periodic Table. Cerium is iron-gray and is about as soft as tin.

Although cerium is not widely known, it is as common in the Earth's crust as copper.

Cerium is (apart from Europium) the most reactive of the rare-earth metals. It oxidizes quickly in moist air and decomposes rapidly in hot water. The metal can ignite when scratched with a knife. It is attacked by both acids and alkalis.

Key facts...
Name: cerium
Symbol: Ce
Atomic number: 58
Atomic weight: 140.1
Position in Periodic Table: inner transition metal; period 6 (lanthanide series)
State at room temperature: solid
Color: iron-gray
Density of solid: 6.771 g/cc
Melting point: 798°C
Boiling point: 3,424°C
Origin of name: named for the asteroid Ceres, which had been discovered in 1801.
Shell pattern of electrons: 2–8–18–20–8–2

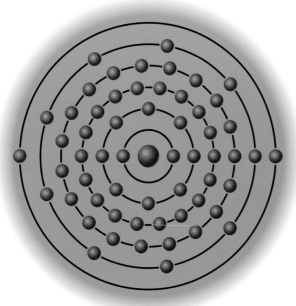

Discovery

Cerium was discovered in Sweden in 1803 by Jöns Jacob Berzelius, Wilhelm Hisinger, and Martin Klaproth.

Technology

It is used for fine polishing of glass (it is faster than rouge), to make porcelain more opaque, and to clear color impurities from glass. It is also widely applied as an alloying metal, for example, in jet engines, where it raises the melting point of the alloy. It goes into incandescent gas mantles and catalysts in self-cleaning oven walls.

Geology

Cerium is never found as a native element. The main cerium minerals are allanite, monazite, cerite, and bastanite. Cerium is difficult to isolate because it is chemically similar to the other lanthanides, and most lanthanide minerals contain thorium, which is radioactive.

Biology

Cerium is not found in living things but is not thought to be particularly harmful.

Cesium (Cs)

Element 55. It is a silvery-white alkali metal.

A member of group 1 on the Periodic Table, it is an extremely soft metal.

Cesium is the most alkaline element. It reacts explosively with cold water and even reacts with ice. It readily combines with oxygen. It also easily loses electrons when struck by light. It is liquid close to room temperature, a property it shares with only gallium and mercury.

Discovery

It was discovered using a spectrometer in 1860 by Robert Bunsen and Gustav Kirchhoff in samples of mineral water from Durkheim, Germany. The clue was the distinctive pair of blue lines they saw.

Technology

Because it easily loses electrons when struck by light, it is used for photoelectric cells. Cesium also goes into atomic clocks. One kg of cesium in outer space could propel a vehicle 140 times as far as burning the same amount of any known liquid or solid. However, it cannot be used this way on Earth.

Geology

It is found in the mineral pollucite, an aluminosilicate. It also appears in rhodizite, a boron mineral.

Biology

Cesium is not found in living things and is rare. It may have the same effects on the body as potassium.

Key facts...

Name: caesium
Symbol: Cs
Atomic number: 55
Atomic weight: 132.9
Position in Periodic Table: group 1 (1) (alkali metal); period 6
State at room temperature: solid (but melts only slightly above this temperature)
Color: silvery-white
Density of solid: 1.87 g/cc
Melting point: 28.44°C
Boiling point: 671°C
Origin of name: named from the Latin *caesius*, meaning sky-blue. It produces two bright lines in the blue part of the spectrum when it is analyzed with a piece of chemical equipment called a mass spectrometer.
Shell pattern of electrons: 2–8–18–18–8–1

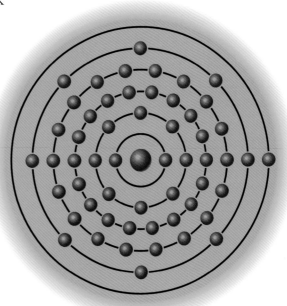

Chlorine (Cl)

Element 17. Chlorine is a greenish-yellow gas and the second lightest halogen in group 7 on the Periodic Table.

Chlorine is never found as a gas in nature. It is an extremely reactive element and a strong oxidizing agent. It is very corrosive and poisonous. It is heavier than air and dissolves in water.

Chlorine is most commonly found as the harmless compound NaCl, common salt.

Discovery

Chlorine was discovered in 1774 by Carl Wilhelm Scheele when he poured concentrated hydrochloric acid onto the mineral pyrolusite (manganese dioxide). He thought the gas was an oxide, but the fact that it was an element was proved, and the element was named by Sir Humphry Davy in 1810.

▶ Chlorine gas has a characteristic green color.

Key facts...
Name: chlorine
Symbol: Cl
Atomic number: 17
Atomic weight: 35.45
Position in Periodic Table: group 7 (17) (halogens); period 3
State at room temperature: gas
Color: greenish-yellow
Density of gas at 20°C: 2.96 g/cc
Melting point: -101°C
Boiling point: -34°C
Origin of name: from the Greek word *chloros*, meaning pale green
Shell pattern of electrons: 2–8–7

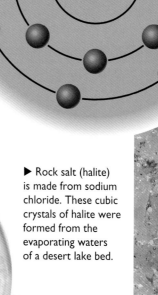

▶ Rock salt (halite) is made from sodium chloride. These cubic crystals of halite were formed from the evaporating waters of a desert lake bed.

Technology

Chlorine is obtained from seawater commercially by electrolysis. Because it is such a deadly poison, it is stored and transported as the liquid HCl, hydrochloric acid.

Chlorine can be used for bleaching and is the most common disinfectant in water supplies. It is also widely applied in the manufacture of plastics such as PVC as well as for medicines, antiseptics, insecticides, paints, and cleaning liquids.

Geology

Chlorine as the compound sodium chloride, common salt, is found in seawater and also as the evaporite rock halite (NaCl).

Biology

It is extremely poisonous even in low concentrations. If chlorine is breathed in, it severely irritates the throat and lungs, and causes severe internal burning. It was used as a chemical weapon in World War I.

Sodium chloride is a food preservative.

▼ In this laboratory demonstration the copper is lowered into a jar containing chlorine. The reaction is violent, producing clouds of copper(II) chloride.

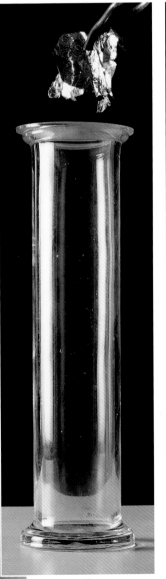

For more on chlorine, see Volume 14: Chlorine, Fluorine, Bromine, and Iodine in the *Elements* set.

Chromium (Cr)

Element 24. Chromium, a steel-gray metal, is a transition metal on the Periodic Table.

Chromium compounds are highly colored. They give color to many natural substances such as emerald (green) and ruby (red) and add red to the paint called Siberian red lead ($PbCrO_4$, crocoite). Chromium metal does not react with water at room temperature.

Discovery

Chromium was discovered in 1797 by the French chemist Nicolas–Louis Vauquelin. Its possible existence was first noticed because of the color that some compounds such as Siberian red lead had, which clearly had nothing to do with their lead content. Vauquelin discovered that the green color of an emerald is also due to chromium.

Technology

Chromium is very hard and can be polished. It is used extensively in plating other materials, especially steel (on cars) and brass (on taps). It resists corrosion, does not tarnish in air or corrode in water, and can be used in an alloy to increase hardness and to resist corrosion. Stainless steel, for example, is an alloy of iron and chromium. Adding it to glass makes the glass emerald green. Chromium is also useful as a catalyst, making a variety of reactions take place faster and more efficiently.

Geology

Chromium is mainly found in chromite ore $Fe(CrO_2)_2$.

Chrome plating is used to protect other metals.

Biology

Chromium is an essential trace element. However, in higher quantities chromium and chromium compounds are toxic.

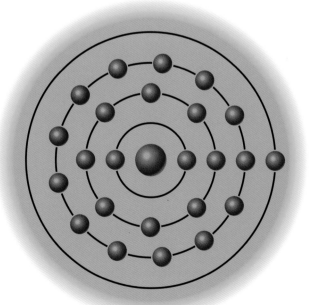

For more on chromium, see Volume 4: Iron, Chromium, and Manganese in the *Elements* set.

Cobalt (Co)

Element 27. A hard, brittle, magnetic transition metal. It is poorly reactive and resists oxidation. The distinctive blue color of cobalt compounds has been used since ancient times.

Cobalt is a scarce metal and usually found as a trace element among ores of other elements such as iron and zinc. Cobalt is very reactive, and finely divided cobalt ignites spontaneously.

Cobalt is both magnetic and has a high melting point, and so can be used where magnetism is required in a hot environment.

Cobalt-60 is a radioactive isotope and a source of gamma rays.

Discovery

Known about as a compound since ancient times, cobalt was first isolated as an element in 1735 by Swedish chemist Georg Brandt.

Technology

The main use of cobalt is as a metal in alloys, both for high temperature permanent magnets and for making very hard steels. Alnico is an alloy of iron, nickel, and cobalt that has a high magnetic strength. Cobalt also gets used in electroplating because it is hard and resists tarnishing. Cobalt phosphate is a blue coloring agent in ceramics and glass. Radioactive isotopes of cobalt have medical applications and also help look for flaws in materials.

Key facts...

Name: cobalt
Symbol: Co
Atomic number: 27
Atomic weight: 58.93
Position in Periodic Table: transition metal, group (9) (cobalt group); period 4
State at room temperature: solid
Color: lustrous, metallic gray
Density of solid: 8.9 g/cc
Melting point: 1,495°C
Boiling point: 2,870°C
Origin of name: from the German word *kobald*, meaning goblin
Shell pattern of electrons: 2–8–15–2

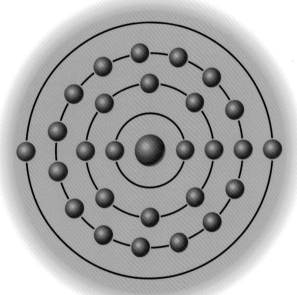

Geology

Cobalt is never found as a native metal. Many sulfide and arsenide ores contain cobalt. The main ore is Co_3S_4, cobaltite. However, it only occurs in small quantities. Cobalt is normally recovered as a by-product of refining ores of nonferrous metals.

Biology

Cobalt is an essential element in blood cells as vitamin B_{12}. Some concentrated meat products that go into drinks contain cobalt to add B_{12} to the diet.

Copper (Cu)

Element 29. Copper is a soft, easily bent metal belonging to the transition metals on the Periodic Table.

It is a very good conductor of electricity and heat. Only silver is a better conductor of electricity than copper.

Native copper was the first metal to be used by people. Records of its use go back over 10,000 years, when it replaced stone. However, it is too soft for good tools and weapons. About 5,500 years ago it was alloyed with tin to make harder bronze. Another alloy, brass, is a mixture of copper and zinc.

Copper does not corrode easily except to produce a thin green protective coat of copper carbonate.

Discovery

Copper has been known since ancient times. It was mined as an ore and refined over 7,000 years ago. It is used on policemen's uniforms for buttons, hence the nickname term for a policeman: cop.

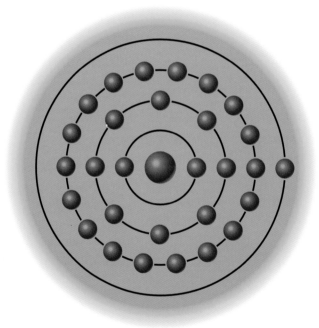

▶ Black copper oxide is heated while hydrogen moves through this reduction tube. The result is pure copper, which shows a characteristically orange color. Particles of copper have also colored the flame, leaving the tube a characteristic green.

Technology

Copper is mainly made into electric wires and alloys with other metals to create bronze or brass (with zinc) or nickel silver (with zinc and nickel—no silver is used at all). Copper also commonly goes into coins. Its low reactivity and attractive color also make it suitable as a roofing material.

Geology

It occurs as native copper and also in many minerals. Chrysocolla is copper silicate; malachite is copper carbonate; bornite and chalcopyrite are copper iron sulfides.

Biology

Copper is a key trace element in all living things.

◀▼ A "seed" crystal of (solid) copper(II) sulfate is suspended by a thread in a solution of copper(II) sulfate. If the beaker is allowed to stand, the water will be lost to the air by evaporation, and the solution will become saturated. At this point copper(II) sulfate solid will form on the seed crystal, and it will grow to form a regular shape—rhombic. Evaporation is one way of separating a mixture.

The solution is a mixture. Because all the components are evenly distributed, the mixture is described as homogeneous.

A copper(II) sulfate solution will conduct electricity, showing that ions are present. The crystal too is ionic.

◀ New York's Statue of Liberty has a pleasing green patina, but the copper is otherwise little affected even after a century of exposure to the weather.

For more on copper, see Volume 5: Copper, Silver, and Gold in the *Elements* set.

Curium (Cm)

Element 96. Curium is a silvery radioactive rare-earth metal in the actinide series on the Periodic Table. It is similar to uranium, plutonium, and americium. Curium is chemically reactive, being more reactive than aluminum.

Curium is produced synthetically. Its compounds include curium fluoride, curium chloride, curium bromide, curium iodide, and curium oxide.

Discovery

It was discovered in 1944 by Glenn T. Seaborg, Ralph A. James, and Albert Ghiorso, using a nuclear reactor to bombard plutonium with accelerated particles.

Technology

It is radioactive and is used in space vehicles because it can provide a compact, long-lived source of electricity. Curium-242 has been used on lunar missions to bombard the surface of the Moon with alpha particles. That helped scientists understand the range and quantity of chemical elements in the Moon's loose surface materials.

Geology

Curium probably occurs in uranium ores in tiny amounts but has never been isolated from natural substances.

Biology

Curium has no biological role. It gives out an extremely toxic form of radiation that can be absorbed by the bones and can disrupt red cell formation.

Key facts...
Name: curium
Symbol: Cm
Atomic number: 96
Atomic weight: 247
Position in Periodic Table: inner transition metal; period 7 (actinide series)
State at room temperature: solid
Color: silvery
Density of solid: 13.51 g/cc
Melting point: 1,340°C
Boiling point: 3,110°C
Origin of name: it was named for Marie Curie.
Shell pattern of electrons: 2–8–18–32–25–9–2

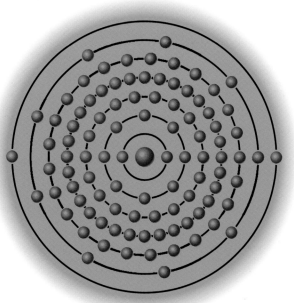

Dubnium (Db)

Element 105. Formerly known as unnilpentium (Unp), hahnium (Ha), and nielsbohrium (Ns).

It is an artificial radioactive element belonging to the transition metals on the Periodic Table.

Discovery

It was discovered in 1967 at the Joint Institute for Nuclear Research in Dubna, Russia, through experiments involving reactions between americium ions and neon ions. In 1970 Albert Ghiorso and others produced dubnium at the University of California at Berkeley. These researchers reacted californium isotopes with a nitrogen ion and berkelium with a nitrogen ion.

Originally, American workers proposed the name hahnium for the late German scientist Otto Hahn, but the International Union of Pure and Applied Chemistry panel members recommended that in 1977 element 105 be renamed dubnium (symbol Db) after the site of the Joint Institute for Nuclear Research in Russia.

Technology

So far, so little of it has been produced that it has no uses, and no one is yet sure of all of its properties.

Geology

It is a synthetic element and so does not occur in the environment.

Biology

Because it is synthetic, it has no role in living things; but since it is radioactive, it is potentially harmful.

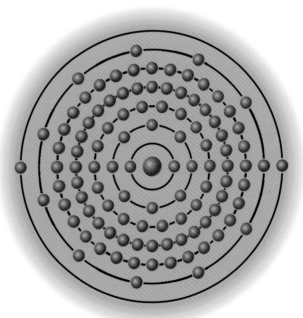

Dysprosium (Dy)

Element 66. A rare-earth element (lanthanide) on the Periodic Table. It is a bright, shiny, silvery-looking, and very reactive metal with a high melting point. Dysprosium is stable in air at room temperature and is soft enough to be cut with a knife. It does not tarnish readily. Dysprosium salts are yellow or yellow-green. All of the salts are very magnetic.

Discovery

It was discovered in 1886 in France by Paul-Émile Lecoq de Boisbaudran, but it was only isolated in the 1950s.

Technology

It readily absorbs neutrons, and in the form of dysprosium oxide it is used in control rods for nuclear reactors. It also goes into an alloy for specialized stainless steels and to make laser materials.

Geology

It does not occur as a native element. It is found in small quantities in minerals such as gadolinite, xenotime, monazite, and bastanite. The most important ores are monaziate and bastnasite. Dysprosium is produced by reducing dysprosium trifluoride using calcium.

Biology

Dysprosium is not found in living things and is not encountered except in specialized laboratories.

Key facts...
Name: dysprosium
Symbol: Dy
Atomic number: 66
Atomic weight: 162.5
Position in Periodic Table: inner transition metal; period 6 (lanthanide series)
State at room temperature: solid
Color: silvery-white
Density of solid: 8.55 g/cc
Melting point: 1,412°C
Boiling point: 2,567°C
Origin of name: from the Greek word *dysprositos*, meaning hard to obtain
Shell pattern of electrons: 2–8–18–28–8–2

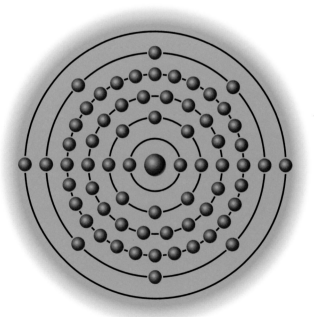

Einsteinium (Es)

Element 99. An artificial transuranium element in the actinide series on the Periodic Table. It was the seventh transuranic element of the actinide series to be discovered.

It was first identified from the debris of thermonuclear bomb tests that occurred in the Pacific Ocean in 1952. It is highly radioactive.

Discovery

It was discovered in 1952 by Albert Ghiorso and others at Argonne, Los Alamos Labs, New Mexico, and the University of California at Berkeley.

The first isotope discovered had an atomic mass of 253 and a half-life of 20 days. More research has discovered fourteen isotopes. The one with the longest half-life (of 275 days) is einsteinium-254.

Technology

Because it has only been isolated in such tiny amounts, nobody has been able to make use of it.

Geology

Because it is an artificial element, it does not occur naturally.

Biology

Since it is an artificial element, it has no role in living things. It is, however, radioactive and therefore potentially hazardous to health.

Key facts...
Name: einsteinium
Symbol: Es
Atomic number: 99
Atomic weight: 252
Position in Periodic Table: inner transition metal; period 7 (actinide series)
State at room temperature: solid
Color: unknown
Density: n/a
Melting point: 860°C
Boiling point: n/a
Origin of name: named for Albert Einstein
Shell pattern of electrons: 2–8–18–32–29–8–2

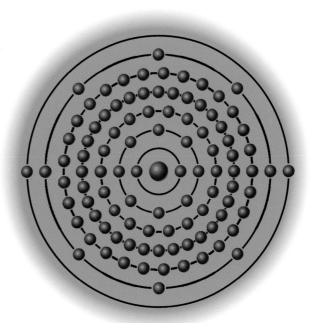

Erbium (Er)

Element 68. A grayish-silver rare-earth metal (lanthanide) on the Periodic Table. It is soft and can be bent easily. It is reasonably stable in air and oxidizes only slowly, unlike many of the rare-earth metals, which tend to tarnish very quickly.

Discovery

Discovered in Sweden in 1843 by Carl Gustaf Mosander, it is one of the three elements separated from the mineral gadolinite, which he called yttria, erbia, and terbia. Erbia and terbia got confused, and the names erbia and terbia were switched. In turn, the erbia isolated was actually found to consist of five oxides, now known as erbia, scandia, holmia, thulia, and ytterbia. It was only in 1905 that pure erbium oxide was isolated. Erbium metal was only isolated in 1934.

Technology

It is important in fiber-optic telecommunications where it is used in light amplifiers. When erbium is alloyed with vanadium, the vanadium becomes more workable. Pink compounds of erbium are used to color glass and enamel.

Geology

It is not found as a native element, but in gadolinite, xenotime, monazite, and bastnasite ores. Erbium oxide is the most common compound. It is a rose-red color and is soluble in most acids.

Biology

It is not found in living things but is not thought to be harmful.

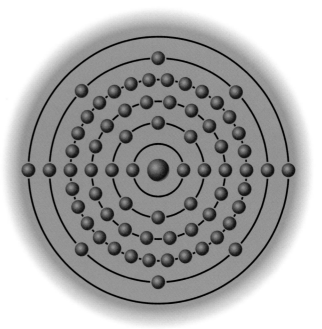

Europium (Eu)

Element 63. A rare-earth metal (lanthanide) on the Periodic Table. It burns spontaneously in air at just over 150°C. It is about as soft as lead and easy to beat into shape. It is the most reactive of the rare-earth metals, and it readily oxidizes in air. It ignites at a temperature of about 150°C.

Discovery

It was discovered in France in 1896 by Eugène-Anatole Demarçay. The pure metal has only recently been isolated.

Technology

Europium is one of the most expensive of the rare earths to produce. It is used in the manufacture of the red phosphors in TV tubes (as europium-activated yttrium vanadate). When it is bombarded with electrons in a cathode-ray tube, it glows red. Europium-doped plastic has been used as a laser material. Europium absorbs neutrons and so is very useful in the control of nuclear fission in nuclear reactors.

Geology

It is not found as a native element, but in gadolinite, xenotime, monazite, and bastnasite ores. It is also found in fission products of uranium, thorium, and plutonium. Europium has also been discovered in the stars.

Biology

It is not found in living things.

Key facts...

Name: europium
Symbol: Eu
Atomic number: 63
Atomic weight: 151.96
Position in Periodic Table: inner transition metal; period 6 (lanthanide series)
State at room temperature: solid
Color: silvery-white
Density of solid: 5.244 g/cc
Melting point: 822°C
Boiling point: 1,527°C
Origin of name: it was named for Europe.
Shell pattern of electrons: 2–8–18–25–8–2

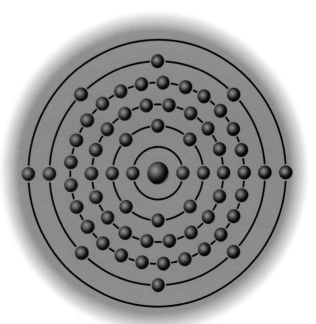

Fermium (Fm)

Element 100. It is an artificial and radioactive rare-earth element in the actinide series on the Periodic Table. Very little is known about fermium.

Discovery

Fermium was first discovered by Albert Ghiorso and others in 1952 at Los Alamos, New Mexico, and the University of California at Berkeley in the radioactive fallout from a nuclear test in the Pacific Ocean.

Technology

Since so little has been isolated, it has no uses.

Geology

It is not found in the environment.

Biology

It is not found in living things.

Key facts...
Name: fermium
Symbol: Fm
Atomic number: 100
Atomic weight: 257
Position in Periodic Table: inner transition metal; period 7 (actinide series)
State at room temperature: solid
Color: unknown
Density of solid: n/a
Melting point: 1,527°C
Boiling point: n/a
Origin of name: named for the scientist Enrico Fermi
Shell pattern of electrons: 2–8–18–32–30–8–2

▼ Fluorine: Polytetrafluoroethylene coatings are found on many household pans to give them their nonstick finish.

The only problem with the material is that it is soft and so can be scratched with metal implements. For this reason wooden or plastic implements need to be used with nonstick pans.

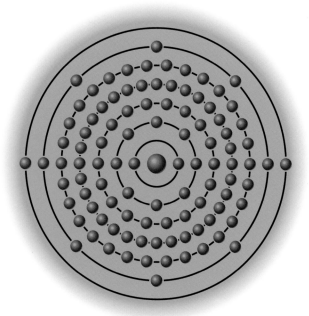

Fluorine (F)

Element 9. Fluorine is the lightest halogen in group 7 on the Periodic Table.

Fluorine, a pale-yellow, very corrosive gas that is slightly heavier than air, is the most reactive chemical element in existence.

Fluorine combines with all other elements except helium, neon, and argon.

It is an extremely poisonous gas.

Key facts...
Name: fluorine
Symbol: F
Atomic number: 9
Atomic weight: 18.99
Position in Periodic Table: group 7 (17), (halogens); period 2
State at room temperature: gas
Color: pale-yellow
Density of gas at 20°C: 1.58 g/cc
Melting point: -219°C
Boiling point: -188°C
Origin of name: from the Latin word *fluere*, meaning to flow
Shell pattern of electrons: 2–7

Discovery

French chemist Henri Moissan discovered fluorine in 1886. Because it is so reactive and difficult to isolate, he eventually had to use an apparatus made from platinum. His success gained him the Nobel Prize for chemistry in 1906.

Technology

It goes into many fluoride-containing plastics. Hydrofluoric acid is used for etching the glass of light bulbs. Fluorochloro-hydrocarbons are used in air conditioning and refrigeration. Fluorides are put into water supplies to help prevent tooth decay.

Geology

It is never found as a native element, but mainly as the mineral fluorite, calcium fluoride (CaF_2), also known as fluorspar and Bohemian emerald.

Biology

Fluorine is found in bones and teeth. Adding fluoride to water has become popular because it helps teeth resist decay.

Fluorite is purple.

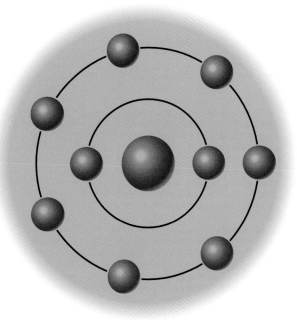

For more on fluorine, see Volume 14: Chlorine, Fluorine, Bromine, and Iodine in the *Elements* set.

The Periodic Table

Actinium (Ac)	89	Calcium (Ca)	20	Fermium (Fm)	100	
Aluminum (Al)	13	Californium (Cf)	98	Fluorine (F)	9	
Antimony (Sb)	51	Carbon (C)	6	Francium (Fr)	87	
Americium (Am)	95	Cerium (Ce)	58	Gadolinium (Gd)	64	
Argon (Ar)	18	Cesium (Cs)	55	Gallium (Ga)	31	
Arsenic (As)	33	Chlorine (Cl)	17	Germanium (Ge)	32	
Astatine (At)	85	Chromium (Cr)	24	Gold (Au)	79	
Barium (Ba)	56	Cobalt (Co)	27	Hafnium (Hf)	72	
Berkelium (Bk)	97	Copper (Cu)	29	Hassium (Hs)	108	
Beryllium (Be)	4	Curium (Cm)	96	Helium (He)	2	
Bismuth (Bi)	83	Dubnium (Db)	105	Holmium (Ho)	67	
Bohrium (Bh)	107	Dysprosium (Dy)	66	Hydrogen (H)	1	
Boron (B)	5	Einsteinium (Es)	99	Indium (In)	49	
Bromine (Br)	35	Erbium (Er)	68	Iodine (I)	53	
Cadmium (Cd)	48	Europium (Eu)	63	Iridium (Ir)	77	

GROUPS ▶

PERIODS ▼

	1 (1)	2 (2)	Transition metals					
			(3)	(4)	(5)	(6)	(7)	(8)
1	1 **H** Hydrogen 1							
2	3 **Li** Lithium 7	4 **Be** Beryllium 9						
3	11 **Na** Sodium 23	12 **Mg** Magnesium 24						
4	19 **K** Potassium 39	20 **Ca** Calcium 40	21 **Sc** Scandium 45	22 **Ti** Titanium 48	23 **V** Vanadium 51	24 **Cr** Chromium 52	25 **Mn** Manganese 55	26 **Fe** Iron 56
5	37 **Rb** Rubidium 85	38 **Sr** Strontium 88	39 **Y** Yttrium 89	40 **Zr** Zirconium 91	41 **Nb** Niobium 93	42 **Mo** Molybdenum 96	43 **Tc** Technetium (99)	44 **Ru** Ruthenium 101
6	55 **Cs** Cesium 133	56 **Ba** Barium 137	71 **Lu** Lutetium 175	72 **Hf** Hafnium 178	73 **Ta** Tantalum 181	74 **W** Tungsten 184	75 **Re** Rhenium 186	76 **Os** Osmium 190
7	87 **Fr** Francium (223)	88 **Ra** Radium (226)	103 **Lr** Lawrencium (260)	104 **Rf** Rutherfordium (261)	105 **Db** Dubnium (262)	106 **Sg** Seaborgium (263)	107 **Bh** Bohrium (262)	108 **Hs** Hassium (265)

- Metals
- Metalloids (semimetals)
- Nonmetals
- Inner transition metals

	57 **La** Lanthanum 139	58 **Ce** Cerium 140	59 **Pr** Praseodymium 141	60 **Nd** Neodymium 144
Lanthanide series				
Actinide series	89 **Ac** Actinium (227)	90 **Th** Thorium (232)	91 **Pa** Protactinium (231)	92 **U** Uranium (238)

Element	No.	Element	No.	Element	No.	Element	No.	Element	No.
Iron (Fe)	26	Neptunium (Np)	93	Protactinium (Pa)	91	Strontium (Sr)	38	Ununoctium (Uuo)	118
Krypton (Kr)	36	Nickel (Ni)	28	Radium (Ra)	88	Sulfur (S)	16	Ununquadium (Uuq)	114
Lanthanum (La)	57	Niobium (Nb)	41	Radon (Rn)	86	Tantalum (Ta)	73	Unununium (Uuu)	111
Lawrencium (Lr)	103	Nitrogen (N)	7	Rhenium (Re)	75	Technetium (Tc)	43	Uranium (U)	92
Lead (Pb)	82	Nobelium (No)	102	Rhodium (Rh)	45	Tellurium (Te)	52	Vanadium (V)	23
Lithium (Li)	3	Osmium (Os)	76	Rubidium (Rb)	37	Terbium (Tb)	65	Xenon (Xe)	54
Lutetium (Lu)	71	Oxygen (O)	8	Ruthenium (Ru)	44	Thallium (Tl)	81	Ytterbium (Yb)	70
Magnesium (Mg)	12	Palladium (Pd)	46	Rutherfordium (Rf)	104	Thorium (Th)	90	Yttrium (Y)	39
Manganese (Mn)	25	Phosphorus (P)	15	Samarium (Sm)	62	Thulium (Tm)	69	Zinc (Zn)	30
Meitnerium (Mt)	109	Platinum (Pt)	78	Scandium (Sc)	27	Tin (Sn)	50	Zirconium (Zr)	40
Mendelevium (Md)	101	Plutonium (Pu)	94	Seaborgium (Sg)	106	Titanium (Ti)	22		
Mercury (Hg)	80	Polonium (Po)	84	Selenium (Se)	34	Tungsten (W)	74		
Molybdenum (Mo)	42	Potassium (K)	19	Silicon (Si)	14	Ununbium (Uub)	112		
Neodymium (Nd)	60	Praseodymium (Pr)	59	Silver (Ag)	47	Ununhexium (Uuh)	116		
Neon (Ne)	10	Promethium (Pm)	61	Sodium (Na)	11	Ununnilium (Uun)	110		

Periodic Table (partial)

Group numbers across: (9) (10) (11) (12) | 3 (13) | 4 (14) | 5 (15) | 6 (16) | 7 (17) | 8 or 0 (18)

(9)	(10)	(11)	(12)	3 (13)	4 (14)	5 (15)	6 (16)	7 (17)	8 or 0 (18)
									2 **He** Helium 4
				5 **B** Boron 11	6 **C** Carbon 12	7 **N** Nitrogen 14	8 **O** Oxygen 16	9 **F** Fluorine 19	10 **Ne** Neon 20
				13 **Al** Aluminum 27	14 **Si** Silicon 28	15 **P** Phosphorus 31	16 **S** Sulfur 32	17 **Cl** Chlorine 35	18 **Ar** Argon 40
27 **Co** Cobalt 59	28 **Ni** Nickel 59	29 **Cu** Copper 64	30 **Zn** Zinc 65	31 **Ga** Gallium 70	32 **Ge** Germanium 73	33 **As** Arsenic 75	34 **Se** Selenium 79	35 **Br** Bromine 80	36 **Kr** Krypton 84
45 **Rh** Rhodium 103	46 **Pd** Palladium 106	47 **Ag** Silver 108	48 **Cd** Cadmium 112	49 **In** Indium 115	50 **Sn** Tin 119	51 **Sb** Antimony 122	52 **Te** Tellurium 128	53 **I** Iodine 127	54 **Xe** Xenon 131
77 **Ir** Iridium 192	78 **Pt** Platinum 195	79 **Au** Gold 197	80 **Hg** Mercury 201	81 **Tl** Thallium 204	82 **Pb** Lead 207	83 **Bi** Bismuth 209	84 **Po** Polonium (209)	85 **At** Astatine (210)	86 **Rn** Radon (222)
109 **Mt** Meitnerium (266)	110 **Uun** Ununnilium (272)	111 **Uuu** Unununium (272)	112 **Uub** Ununbium (277)		114 **Uuq** Ununquadium (289)		116 **Uuh** Ununhexium (289)		118 **Uuo** Ununoctium (293)

61 **Pm** Promethium (145)	62 **Sm** Samarium 150	63 **Eu** Europium 152	64 **Gd** Gadolinium 157	65 **Tb** Terbium 159	66 **Dy** Dysprosium 163	67 **Ho** Holmium 165	68 **Er** Erbium 167	69 **Tm** Thulium 169	70 **Yb** Ytterbium 173
93 **Np** Neptunium (237)	94 **Pu** Plutonium (244)	95 **Am** Americium (243)	96 **Cm** Curium (247)	97 **Bk** Berkelium (247)	98 **Cf** Californium (251)	99 **Es** Einsteinium (252)	100 **Fm** Fermium (257)	101 **Md** Mendelevium (258)	102 **No** Nobelium (259)

Understanding equations

As you read through Volumes 1 to 15 in the Elements set, you will notice that many pages contain equations using symbols. Symbols make it easy for chemists to write out the reactions that are occurring in a way that allows a better understanding of the processes involved. If you are not familiar with these symbols, these pages explain them.

Symbols for the elements

The basis for the modern use of symbols for elements dates back to the 19th century. At that time a shorthand was developed using the first letter of the element wherever possible.

Thus O stands for oxygen, H stands for hydrogen, and so on. However, if we were to use only the first letter, there could be some confusion. For example, nitrogen and nickel would both use the symbols N. To overcome this problem, many element symbols take the first two letters of the full name, with the second letter in lowercase. So, although nitrogen is N, nickel becomes Ni. Not all symbols come from the English name; many use the Latin name instead. That is why, for example, gold is not G but Au (from the Latin *aurum*), and sodium has the symbol Na (from the Latin *natrium*).

Compounds of elements are made by combining letters. So, the molecule carbon

Written and symbolic equations

In this book important chemical equations are briefly stated in words (they are called word equations) and are then shown in their symbolic form along with the states.

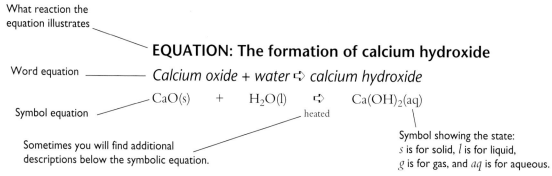

What reaction the equation illustrates

EQUATION: The formation of calcium hydroxide

Word equation ———— *Calcium oxide + water ⟹ calcium hydroxide*

Symbol equation ———— $CaO(s)$ + $H_2O(l)$ ⟹ $Ca(OH)_2(aq)$

heated

Sometimes you will find additional descriptions below the symbolic equation.

Symbol showing the state: s is for solid, l is for liquid, g is for gas, and aq is for aqueous.

Diagrams

Some of the equations are shown as graphic representations.

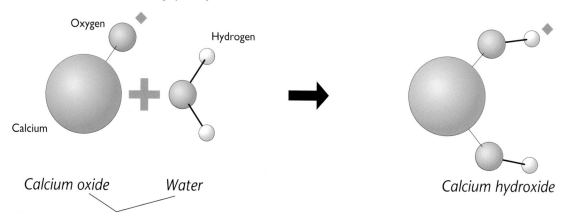

Oxygen

Hydrogen

Calcium

Calcium oxide   *Water*

Calcium hydroxide

Sometimes the written equation is broken up and put below the relevant stages in the graphic representation.

monoxide is CO. By using lowercase letters for the second letter of an element, it is possible to show that cobalt, symbol Co, is not the same as the molecule carbon monoxide, CO.

However, the letters can be made to do much more than this. In many molecules atoms combine in unequal numbers. So, for example, carbon dioxide has one atom of carbon for every two of oxygen. That is shown by using the number 2 beside the oxygen, and the symbol becomes CO_2.

In practice some groups of atoms combine as a unit with other substances. Thus, for example, calcium bicarbonate (one of the compounds used in some antacid pills) is written $Ca(HCO_3)_2$. This shows that the part of the substance inside the parentheses reacts as a unit, and the 2 outside the parentheses shows the presence of two such units.

Some substances attract water molecules to themselves. To show this, a dot is used. So, the blue form of copper sulfate is written $CuSO_4.5H_2O$. In this case five molecules of water attract to one of copper sulfate. When you see the dot, you know that this water can be driven off by heating; it is part of the crystal structure.

In a reaction substances change by rearranging the combinations of atoms. The way they change is shown by using the chemical symbols, placing those that will react (the starting materials, or reactants) on the left and the products of the reaction on the right. Between the two an arrow shows which way the reaction is going.

It is possible to describe a reaction in words. That produces word equations, which are given throughout Volumes 1 to 15. However, it is easier to understand what is happening by using an equation containing symbols. They are also given in many places. They are not shown when the equations are very complex.

In any equation both sides balance; that is, there must be an equal number of like atoms on both sides of the arrow. When you try to write down reactions, you, too, must balance your equation; you cannot have a few atoms left over at the end!

The symbols in parentheses are abbreviations for the physical state of each substance taking part, so that (s) is used for solid, (l) for liquid, (g) for gas, and (aq) for an aqueous solution, that is, a solution of a substance dissolved in water.

Atoms and ions
Each sphere represents a particle of an element. A particle can be an atom or an ion. Each atom or ion is associated with other atoms or ions through bonds – forces of attraction. The size of the particles and the nature of the bonds can be extremely important in determining the nature of the reaction or the properties of the compound.

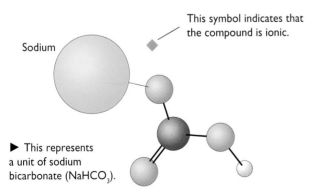

Sodium

This symbol indicates that the compound is ionic.

▶ This represents a unit of sodium bicarbonate ($NaHCO_3$).

The term "unit" is sometimes used to simplify the representation of a combination of ions.

Chemical symbols, equations, and diagrams
The arrangement of any molecule or compound can be shown in one of the two ways shown below, depending on which gives the clearer picture. The left-hand image is called a ball-and-stick diagram because it uses rods and spheres to show the structure of the material. This example shows water, H_2O. There are two hydrogen atoms and one oxygen atom.

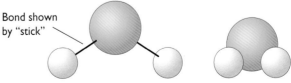

Bond shown by "stick"

Colors too
The colors of each of the particles help differentiate the elements involved. The diagram can then be matched to the written and symbolic equation given with the diagram. In the case above, oxygen is red, and hydrogen is gray.

Set Index

A

A-bomb **15:** 38
Ac *see* actinium
acetate **8:** 41
acetic acid **1:** 31, **7:** 33, **8:** 29
acetone **7:** 34, **8:** 28
acetylene **8:** 29, **14:** 22
acid **1:** 12, 18, 19, 20, 22, 23, 34, 35, 36, 37, **2:** 31, **3:** 12, 21, 29, 39, 42, **7:** 14, 33, **13:** 19, 26, 27
acid burn **1:** 24, **13:** 26, **2:** 32, 33, **3:** 13, **4:** 10, **7:** 40, 42, 43, **10:** 12, **11:** 31, 32, **12:** 13, 29, 42, **13:** 18, 19, 22, 23
acidity **1:** 20–21
acidosis **1:** 28
acids **9:** 11
acid soil **4:** 17
actinides, actinide series **16:** 8 *see also* Periodic Table
actinium (Ac) **16:** 17
activated charcoal **8:** 22, 23, **14:** 27

addition polymer **8:** 32–35
adhesive **3:** 22, 23, **12:** 20
admiralty brass **5:** 18
adsorption **14:** 27, **7:** 35, **8:** 23
aeration **12:** 8, 9
aeroembolism **11:** 7
Ag *see* silver
agate **9:** 13, 14
Agent Orange **14:** 29
air **11:** 38, **12:** 6, 7, 17
air bag **11:** 29
Al *see* aluminum
alchemists, alchemy **1:** 22, 23, **15:** 11
alclad **7:** 23
alcohols **8:** 28
algae **3:** 4, 40, **11:** 43
algal blooms **11:** 43
alkali **1:** 20, 34, 35, **2:** 5, 32, **7:** 14, 33, 36, **11:** 12, 14, 15, 39
alkaline **1:** 20, 32, 33, **2:** 6, 31, 32
alkanes (paraffins) **8:** 28
alloy **4:** 34, 35, 36–37, 40, **5:** 20, **6:** 20, 22, 41, **7:** 22–23, **9:** 31, **10:** 40, 41
alpha particle **15:** 8, 42
alpha radiation **15:** 8, 9
alum **7:** 4, 7, 36, **8:** 15
alumina **7:** 16, 17, 18, 19, 34
alumina-silica gel **8:** 27, **1:** 26, 36
aluminum (Al) **See Vol. 7 and Vol. 16:** 18–19; **1:** 26, 36, **2:** 32, **4:** 22, 23, **5:** 21, 35, **6:** 22, **9:** 11, 20, 26, 34, 37, **10:** 39, **11:** 37, **12:** 10, 38, **15:** 9
aluminum foil **7:** 21, 30
aluminum hydroxide **7:** 36, 37, 38
aluminum oxide **7:** 7, 14, 16, 17, 18, 34, 35, **8:** 20, 21, **9:** 13, **12:** 11, 39, **4:** 33
aluminum silicate **9:** 26
aluminum sulfate **7:** 7, 36, 38, **8:** 15
Am *see* americium
amalgam **5:** 35, 42, **6:** 26, 36, 37, **7:** 22, **14:** 19
amalgamation **5:** 39
Amatol **11:** 27
americium (Am) **16:** 21
amethyst **9:** 12
amino acids **8:** 36
ammonia **1:** 16–17, 22, 26, 27, 32, **2:** 28, 29, **7:** 36, **11:** 12–17, 36, 37, **13:** 36, 43, **14:** 17, 34, 39
ammonia fountain **11:** 15
ammonia solution **5:** 27
ammonite **3:** 9
ammonium chloride **1:** 22, 23, **2:** 28, 29, **4:** 41, **6:** 14, 15, **11:** 13, **14:** 34
ammonium dichromate **11:** 24, 25
ammonium hydroxide **11:** 12
ammonium nitrate **11:** 13, 27
ammonium nitrite **11:** 27
ammonium perchlorate **12:** 39, **14:** 24
ammonium sulfate **7:** 36, **11:** 14, **13:** 43

ammunition **10:** 15, **11:** 27
amorphous **9:** 38
amphiboles **9:** 24
amphoteric **6:** 10, **7:** 14
anesthetics **14:** 5
anglesite **10:** 7
anhydrous **13:** 34
anions **3:** 29, **6:** 12,
annealing **7:** 20, **9:** 41
anode **2:** 23, 26, **3:** 37, **6:** 12, 13, **7:** 19, 25, **10:** 11
anodizing **7:** 26
antacid **2:** 31, **3:** 5, 42, 47, **8:** 15
anthracite **8:** 7
antibacterial agent **6:** 38
antimony (Sb) **See Vol. 16:** 20; **10:** 15, 40
antimony-133 **15:** 29
antioxidant **11:** 10
antiseptic **14:** 41
apatite **11:** 42
approximate relative atomic mass **16:** 7
aqua fortis **1:** 26, **11:** 36
aqua regia **1:** 22, 26, **5:** 41, **11:** 36
aquamarine **9:** 23, **12:** 10
aquifers **2:** 20
architectural brass **5:** 19
Ar *see* argon
argon (Ar) **See Vol. 1 and Vol. 16:** 22; **4:** 30, **11:** 8, 9, **12:** 17, **15:** 11
arsenic (As) **See Vol. 16:** 23; **2:** 30, **13:** 42
As *see* arsenic
asbestos **14:** 20
asphalt **8:** 26, 27
aspirin **1:** 30
astatine (At) **16:** 24
At *see* astatine
atmosphere **3:** 12, **11:** 6, **12:** 6, 8, 12
atom, atoms **1–15:** 47, **16–18:** 57; **1:** 4, 38, **8:** 15, **15:** 4, 7, **16:** 4, 11
atomic bomb **15:** 38, 39
atomic mass **16:** 15 *see also* approximate relative atomic mass
atomic number **16:** 4, 7, 15
atomic weight **16:** 15
Au *see* gold
augite **9:** 24
aurora **12:** 7, **11:** 7
Australia **7:** 11
azide **11:** 29

B

B *see* boron
Ba *see* barium
background radiation **15:** 14–15
Bacon, Roger **11:** 26
bacteria **13:** 8, 20
Baekland, Leo **8:** 31
Bakelite **8:** 31
baking powder **2:** 30
baking soda **2:** 28, 30, **8:** 14
barite **13:** 12, **16:** 24, 25
barium (Ba) **16:** 25
barium chlorate **14:** 24
barium-142 **15:** 28
barium peroxide **4:** 22
barium sulfate **13:** 12
barometer **6:** 30

basalt **9:** 24, 43, **15:** 18
base **1:** 22, 23, 32–33, 34, **2:** 32, **3:** 21, 25
base bullion **10:** 10
basic-oxygen furnace process **4:** 30, 31
basic-oxygen process **12:** 27
battery **4:** 41, **6:** 5, 12, **10:** 28, **13:** 30, 31
bauxite **7:** 10–11, 13, 14, 16, 18
Bayer, Karl Joseph **7:** 12
Bayer process **7:** 14, 16
Be *see* beryllium
becquerel **15:** 13, 22
Becquerel, A. H. **6:** 35, **15:** 5, 12, 22
bell-making bronze **5:** 21
bends **11:** 7
Benin bronze **5:** 19
benzene ring **8:** 33
berkelium (Bk) **16:** 26
beryl **7:** 8, **9:** 22
beryllium (Be) **See Vol. 16:** 27; **7:** 8, **9:** 22
Bessemer Converter **4:** 31, **12:** 27
Bessemer, Sir Henry **4:** 31
beta particle **15:** 8
beta radiation **15:** 8, 9
Bh *see* bohrium
Bi *see* bismuth
bicarbonate **1:** 29, 31
Big Bang **15:** 7
biotite **7:** 6, **9:** 26
bismuth (Bi) **See Vol. 16:** 28; **10:** 11
Bk *see* berkelium
black phosphorus **11:** 38
blast furnace **4:** 24, 25, 26, 27, **12:** 26
bleach **4:** 42, **12:** 21, **13:** 18, 20–21, **14:** 14, 15, 24
bleaching agent **13:** 18–21
blood **12:** 15
blood (salts) **2:** 18, 19
blue-green algae **11:** 18, 19, 22
Blue John **14:** 8, 36
blue vitriol **5:** 24, **13:** 32
body **2:** 18,19, **3:** 5, 32
bog iron ore **4:** 13
bohrium (Bh) **16:** 29
bond **1:** 9, 11, **2:** 23, **3:** 47
bone **3:** 5, 32
Bordeaux mixture **5:** 23, **13:** 34, 42
bornite **5:** 6
boron (B) **16:** 30
boron oxide **9:** 38
borosilicate glass **9:** 39, **16:** 30
Br *see* bromine
brass **5:** 18–19, 20, 27, **6:** 4, 20, **10:** 15
braze **5:** 18, **7:** 20
Brazil **7:** 11
breeder reactor **15:** 35
brimstone **13:** 4, 5, 10
brimstone and treacle **13:** 42
brine **1:** 14, 15, **2:** 12, 13, 25, 26, 27, 28, 29, 40, **6:** 33, **14:** 18, 19, 20
bromide **14:** 4
bromine (Br) **See Vol. 14 and Vol. 16:** 31; **8:** 23
bromothymol blue **1:** 21
bronze **5:** 20–21, 27, 34, **6:** 20, 21, **10:** 40, 41